The Med School Survival Kit:

How to Breeze Through Med School While Crushing Your Exams

By Wendell Cole, M.D.

The Med School Survival Kit:

How to Breeze Through Med School While Crushing Your Exams

By Wendell Cole, M.D.

Creator of www.iamdrcole.com

ISBN: 978-1-7323843-0-9

DEDICATION(S)

I dedicate this book to my mom and dad. If it weren't for you two I wouldn't have made it to the point in my life that I am at right now. You pushed me to excel. Love you both.

This book is also dedicated to you, the person reading this - to all the medical students who have sacrificed and will sacrifice years of your life to serve people. You are truly an inspiration. This is also for all the pre-med students who believe a life in the medical field without balance isn't achievable.

TABLE OF CONTENTS

INTRODUCTION

Welcome to the first edition of *The Med School Survival Kit: How to Breeze Through Med School While Crushing Your Exams!* I made this book for you, and here's why. It is a common misconception that medical school will take over your life completely and that you will spend 4 years living in the dark ages. I personally have found this to not be true.

When I started medical school, I was running my first startup app business, Luxevents (RIP, it didn't go as planned but that's okay) so I had to figure out how to manage a business plus school. Since then, a classmate and I have been able to open a real estate business (Touchdown Houses LLC), and complete real estate deals in less than six months.

In addition, I was an active representative in a network marketing company, and I was able to travel across the United States and internationally all while in medical school with my old hashtag #TravelingMedStudent. **I also ended up matching into one of the most competitive specialties, Orthopaedic Surgery.** So, it is possible to have fun and still live the life you want to; it's all about how you view and approach things.

I was always asked, "How do you do all of this while in medical school?" I was told "You must just be really smart," and "You're not in medical school, there is no way." I was asked, "How?" so many times that I decided to go ahead and write a book about it and help whoever I can.

The purpose of this book is to walk you through your medical school years and show you how to study effectively. You will learn what resources you can use to help guide you through the four years of medical school so you don't waste countless hours doing unnecessary things. I hope that this book adds value to your life, helps to guide you, saves you time, and makes your life easier on this marvelous medical school journey.

-Wendell Cole, M.D.

CH 1.
HOW TO BREEZE THROUGH MED SCHOOL

Why would you want to "breeze" through medical school? What does that mean? Now if you think that means you are just going to sit back and do nothing and the information will somehow magically enter your brain while you are on a beach sipping pina coladas and getting a massage, no, you are mistaken. When I say breeze through med school, I mean that you can make it through medical school while actually living the life that you want to live. You don't have to be stressed out all of the time, you don't have to study 24/7, and you don't have to live without a social life (most of the time).

MEDICAL SCHOOL MINDSET

First off, congratulations on being accepted to medical school! That is a big feat and a big hurdle that many people don't make. So congrats, you are now officially 10% of a doctor! Now you may be like me in some areas. When I was about to start medical school, I almost had an "Oh I need to have all my fun now and live life!" moment, because the next 4 years of my life I will be stuck in books. Everything that I heard about medical school was that it was hard and grueling. I mean, you see the memes and hear the rumors.

I was excited to be starting the medical field journey, but it was bittersweet because I thought I would also become a robot.

I previously thought that medical school was going to control me and that I was going to succumb to it every day, but that mindset quickly changed. During this period of my life, I was running a business and needed to allocate time in order to get my necessary tasks completed. Something deep within me said no, **I am going to control medical school** and I am going to be in charge of how I experience the next couple of years.

Starting off in my 1st year, I would say to myself, "Ok, today medical school gets three hours of my time to study, and x, y, and z is what I'm going to accomplish." I also told myself I absolutely had to finish what I needed to in that timeframe. So, for example, if I finished classes at 4 pm, med school would get my undivided attention from 5-8pm. Since I KNEW that this was my allocated time to study for the day, I didn't have any distractions. I wasn't on Facebook or Instagram goofing around. I wasn't texting everybody and on the phone all of the time. I was in the moment. Then the time from 4-5pm and 8pm-8am was free for whatever I wanted to do.That's 13 free hours of a 24 hour day if you missed that (7 hours after you minus 6 hours of sleep)!

One of the best pieces of study advice that I got was to **study like the test is tomorrow**. You can do the same. Have you ever had to write a paper before and you were given 3 weeks to finish it? You may have worked on it here and there, kind of, but it took you some time until you got to the point where you said, "Ok, I'll sit down and do it now." Do you think you would use your time more efficiently if you were told to write a paper that will be due in 3 weeks, or you were given a paper to write that you had to turn in tonight by 11:59 pm? Exactly. If you had to turn the paper in tonight or else you got a zero, you would be focused on the paper and probably wouldn't have many distractions. Apply that same concept/mindset to studying.

The mindset that you are going to take control of the next 4 years of your life and that you are in control of how you spend your time and how you experience life is something powerful. Many times because it's the "norm" and you think that if you aren't spending 10 hours a day studying and sleeping at the library like everybody else then you aren't being a good student. That's not the case; know that you are in control, not the other way around.

COMPARING YOURSELF

This is a thing in medical school that you need to address from the start. I think it's so important that it needed its own mini-section. Comparing yourself to your classmates is inherently a hard thing not to do. In many schools, there is a competitive nature to be at the top of the class. You must know that, as humans, we instinctively want to make ourselves look good and avoid looking bad. Sometimes people will hold back resources or lie about the grades that they get in a class to make themselves look better.

If you internalize that and think that you are doing badly when you compare yourself to others, it can have detrimental effects. You have to understand that not everybody is the same. Just because a classmate scores higher than you doesn't mean anything. It may be that they are strong in biochemistry, but you are better at physiology. Worry about yourself and give all of your efforts to excel at the best of YOUR OWN abilities. Run your own race.

BELIEVING IN YOURSELF

This is a big one. I've seen it many times. People think that they can't get an A in medical school or get a high STEP 1 score from the start, and it hurts them. They come in saying, "I know I'm not one of the A students," or "I don't think I can get a 255 on STEP 1, I'll just aim for a 220."

What that does is it stifles you from the beginning. Once you speak or think that way, your actions tend to correlate. At first, it will start off small. So instead of concentrating and doing that extra question, going that extra step to understand the pathophysiology, or remembering that drug side effect, you say "Meh, I can miss this one."

Then you say "Meh, I can miss this one question too," again when another topic comes up... then again... and then you say "Forget studying I'll just take a lower grade on this test and do better on the next one." It becomes a spiral. After a while it becomes detrimental and you'll eventually turn into the "Meh" emoji.

This is the **number one** thing I would say to do: **believe in yourself**. Nobody else will. If you believe that you can make it into the Alpha Omega Alpha (AOA) honor society and you state that from the time you start, then you can. You can make all A's. You CAN be in the top 1% of your class even if you weren't in undergrad/masters.

I mean, my MCAT scores weren't the best and some sections were awful... I used to hate reading. I got a 6 in the verbal section, (This is back on the old MCAT when sections were scored 1-15), but I ended up scoring above the national average on my USMLE STEP 1 and STEP 2 exams (234 STEP 1, 259 STEP 2 - I tend to be straightforward about my scores). Believing in and trusting yourself will get you a long way in the field of medicine and in life.

I interviewed one of my high-achieving classmates who scored 250+ on his STEP 1 exam for a podcast, and I asked him about the mindset he had going into medical school. His background was different from the typical biology pre-med track; he had a degree in computer science. He said it was a field where he failed many times when doing projects. So he wasn't afraid of failure.

He brought that same mindset to medical school; he was not afraid to put his all out there on a test and fail doing it. Failing wasn't the end of the world - when you fail, you look back and re-evaluate yourself, see where you went wrong, and adjust accordingly. Deep down, he had a belief system set that he could do anything he put his mind to. If you adopt this same system of believing in yourself, I promise you it will take you a long way. Don't limit yourself and on what you think you can achieve during medical school.

GOAL SETTING

You need to figure out what you want to get out of medical school. What are you trying to do? For me, my goal was to get all A's, but I was also ok with getting some B's. Some schools don't do the ABCDF grading system and its pass/fail. I knew that the big test that mattered was the STEP 1 exam and that I wanted to do well on it.

What's your goal? Do you want to get all A's, be AOA, president of your Student Government Association (SGA), and president of your student organizations? Do you want to accomplish all of that while going out every night too? I'm not saying that's impossible to do but it's smart to set realistic goals. What do you really see yourself doing? Do you want to be able to spend time with your significant other every day, workout daily, get A's and B's, and get a 250 on STEP 1? Figure it out.

Having a clear understanding of what you want to accomplish in the upcoming years will help you organize your daily activities and habits accordingly, and give you a sense of what you need to do to make your goals come through. You can make a vision board and hang it up in your room, or you can write it down on a piece of paper. Write down what's really important to you. Think about your career, social life, and relationships. You can use my goal sheet provided at the end of this chapter to help guide you through it.

One thing you start to realize is that you are slowly beginning to form the habits that will follow you throughout your career. Meaning, you will realize that if in medical school you weren't a person that made time to exercise and be with loved ones, in residency you probably won't, and it will be the same when you are an attending physician. Know what you want and start to implement it now.

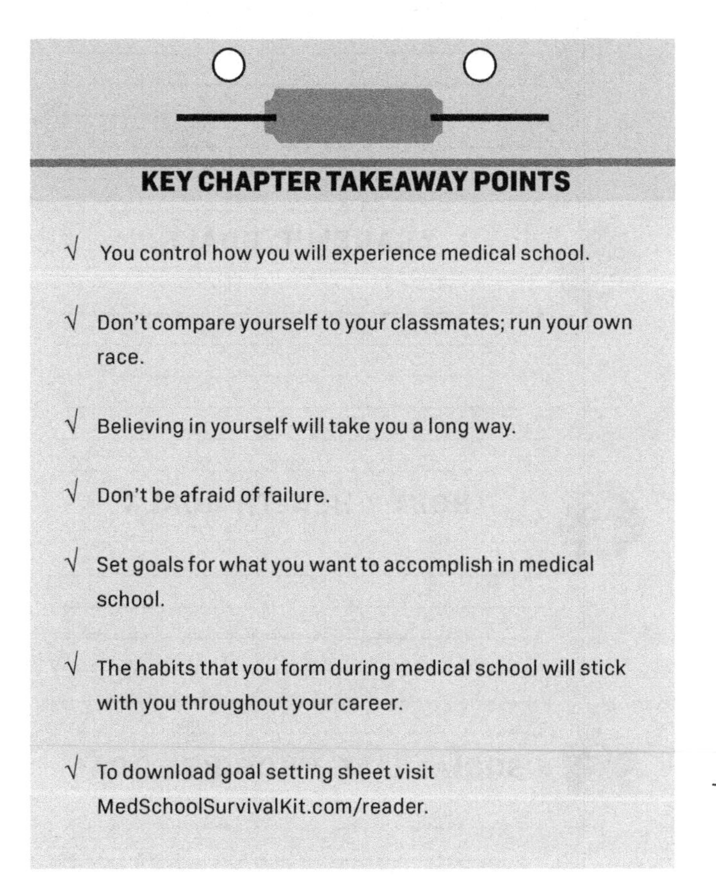

KEY CHAPTER TAKEAWAY POINTS

√ You control how you will experience medical school.

√ Don't compare yourself to your classmates; run your own race.

√ Believing in yourself will take you a long way.

√ Don't be afraid of failure.

√ Set goals for what you want to accomplish in medical school.

√ The habits that you form during medical school will stick with you throughout your career.

√ To download goal setting sheet visit MedSchoolSurvivalKit.com/reader.

#GOALS

WHAT DO I WANT OUT OF MED SCHOOL?

RELATIONSHIP / FAMILY GOALS

ACADEMIC GOALS

BODY / HEALTH GOALS

SOCIAL LIFE / HOBBIES GOAL

CH 2.
STUDY SCHEDULE

The MVP of questions: "What was your study schedule like in medical school?"

UNDERSTANDING THE TRANSITION

While I was in undergrad, I was taking around 16 credit hours per semester. I used to take notes on each powerpoint for every class and was very diligent and thorough. For a test in a class in undergrad, I may have had 8 PowerPoint presentations that were 33 slides long each that I would have to know for the exam.

I'd think "Man! This is a lot of information for me to remember by next week. How do they expect us to know all of this?" Looking back now, I realize how good I had it! When you are in medical school, it switches to "Man! I have 8, 100 slide PowerPoint presentations to learn for one class, and I have 4 classes!" Sheesh! I was complaining for no reason back then!

At some point, you will most likely hear that studying in medical school is like drinking water from a fire hydrant, and it is. One of my professors, Dr. Patrickson, also told us that, "It is like drinking water from a fire hydrant, but with time, you learn how to drink very quickly." You will learn to understand how to process all of the information that's getting thrown at you.

When we talk about the transition from medical school, you have to understand that it's going to be harder. I DO have good news though...I just saved a bunch of money by switching my car insurance...Just kidding. The good news is that the information itself will not be hard, it is just a matter of learning to process the pure volume. There are going be classes that will challenge you. There are going to be obstacles that you are going to have to overcome. All of this is a part of the process. You are only facing what other successful men/women have met, meaning you're only doing what other students have done before you. **Your medical school would not have accepted you if they thought that you could not handle the information.**

REPETITION

So let's talk about studying. Repetition is the father of learning. I'm sure you've heard that before in some song or stated in some sense (I think Lil Wayne said that in the song Shoot Me Down). The more times that you view the material, the easier it will be to remember.

I kind of see myself as the "lazy studier". I'd rather look at material for 10 minutes a day for 10 days than spend 100 minutes on one day trying to learn the same amount of information. When you look over concepts multiple times, you have time to sleep on it. You process information when you sleep. There are studies that show that you retain information better after sleeping. Just Google "Sleep and Learning" or "Sleep and Memory" to see for yourself.

APPROACHING A BLOCK OF INFORMATION + CREATING A SCHEDULE

Now, think of information as a huge block that you have to learn and understand. Every day, every time you look at the material, every time you read or watch a video, you're chipping away little by little at this huge block of information. If you set it up so you are doing this daily, by the end of the week you will have mastered the information.

The 1st pass - Getting those toenails wet. I suggest that you approach learning new information by reviewing the subjects that you will be learning in class the day **before**. Spend about ten/fifteen minutes or so per subject and get the big picture.

You aren't getting into the details of everything yet. Watching a video on the subject is an easy way, or you can read the chapter in the book. This way when you are in class, you know what is going on and you will be able to ask **informed questions**.

The 2nd pass- Up to your knees in the water. Now your second time seeing the information is when you go to class the next day. If you don't waste your time, sit there, and pay attention, you can get a lot out of class. Treat class like an in-depth study session since you already have a big picture of what is going on. **Ask informed questions and make sure you understand everything before you leave class/lecture.**

3rd pass- Thighs deep into the water and a couple splashes on your stomach. The third time we take a chop at this block is going to be later on that afternoon of the lecture. So if you think about it now, you've already spent about an hour and a half or so absorbing the information before this point. Take another look through it to make sure that you got all of the high points that you need to understand. You are solidifying what you already learned. So within a 24-hour timespan, you have processed the information three times.

4th pass- Then the day after that, when studying, review what you learned yesterday at the beginning of your study session for 25 minutes or so. Start off your study session with about 10 practice questions or so to test your knowledge and see what exactly you need to focus on within that material. (Again, keywords - do questions!)

5th pass- Do pass 4 again the next day for 15 minutes (less time), and so on and so on. Again, do questions on the topic BEFORE you start to review.

The result of using this method is that you will be spending LESS time studying outside of class.

Keep it simple and study the material you will learn tomorrow, today. Learn it tomorrow and learn it again tomorrow night. Do that every day and you will be successful.

HERE IS AN EXAMPLE BREAKDOWN OF REPETITION IN A STUDY SCHEDULE :

Sunday	15 minutes review for: X,Y,Z - Total time - **45 minutes**
Monday	**Class:** 1.5 hr per class - 4.5hr That night 45 min for classes X,Y,Z - 2hr 15min 10 min review for classes X,Y,Z tomorrow - 30 min Total study time outside class - **2hr 45min**
Tuesday	Class: 1.5 hr per class - 4.5 hr That night: 10 questions + Monday review on X,Y,Z - 30 min That night, study 45 min X,Y,Z - 2hr 15 min Review X,Y,Z tomorrow - 30 min Total study time outside class: **3hrs 15min**
Wednesday	Class:1.5 hr per class - 4.5hrs That night: 10 questions over Monday/Tuesday - 40 min That night, study 45 min X,Y,Z - 2hr 15 min Review X,Y,Z, tomorrow - 30 min Total study time outside class: **3hrs 25min**
Thursday	That night: 10 questions over Monday/Tuesday/Wednesday - 50 min That night, study 45 min X,Y,Z - 2hr 15 min Review X,Y,Z, tomorrow - 30 min Total study time outside class: **3hrs 35min**
Friday	That night: 10 questions over Monday/Tuesday- 60 min That night, study 45 min X,Y,Z - 2hr 15 min. Review X,Y,Z, tomorrow - 30 min Total study time outside class: **3hrs 45min**
Saturday	Questions on all topics - **3hrs** Reviewing topics weak on - **2hrs**

Next Week - add at least 10 minutes before each study day session to review topics that you looked over this week.

SAMPLE DAILY SCHEDULE :

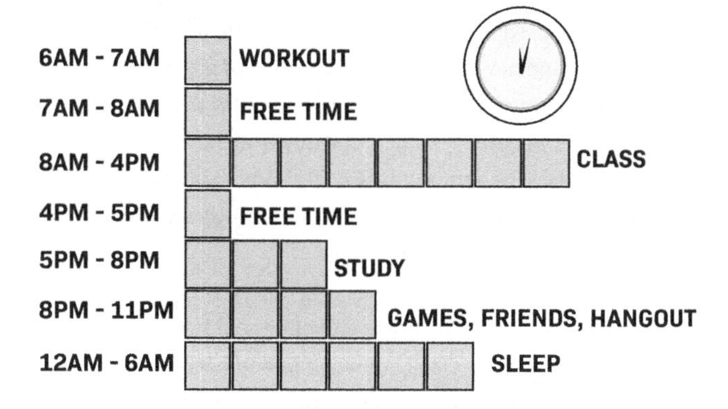

It IS possible to have a life. You can play around with it and add an extra TWO hours to study and would STILL HAVE TIME.

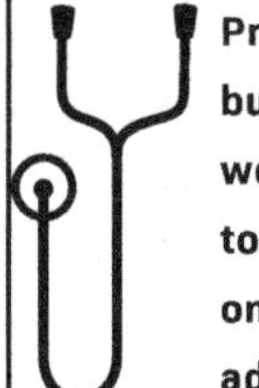

Pro Tip: Study schedules are a great outline to go by, but life will happen and things will get in the way. You won't always be on schedule. So plan for the unexpected to happen. Don't get too stressed out when you aren't on schedule, just make some adjustments. Champions adjust. Medicine isn't scheduled.

CLASS

Now, let's quickly talk about going to class. Depending on your institution, this is something you may or may not have to go to. Class could be online or in person. Some of your curriculums may be group-based learning (GBL) instead of lecture style. I would recommend **if** you go to class, that you stay off of social media.

Sit there, pay attention, and actually attempt to understand the information. Ask questions and become actively engaged with your team (if GBL). When you ask questions, you remember things better because you are engaging your brain.

Take this. Say you have a class that's about an hour and 30 minutes long and you go and dilly dally in class. You kind of pay attention. You kind of don't. Guys: you're looking at that girl with the nice dress, and ladies you are looking at that guy with the muscle shirt on (or whatever type of person you are into), and they have you daydreaming about them! I mean, you're imagining your whole future life together at this point!

Later on that day when you go home and open your book, you think about what you learned in class but won't remember anything. You will be thinking of that woman's (man's) well-formed body at the beach coming out of the water with the sun shining ever so brightly while they gaze at you in bliss, instead of cardiac embryology (not speaking from experience here or anything). Now you have to spend hours learning the information for the first time.

In many cases you are paying tens of thousands of dollars to get an education in medical school, so make that investment count. In lecture, use your teachers and ask them questions and make them work to teach you and have you understand.

KEY CHAPTER TAKEAWAY POINTS

√ Repetition is key.

√ Every day, study what you learned the day before, what you learned that day, and what you will learn tomorrow.

√ Repetition is key.

√ Start to incorporate review questions the day after you learn the topic.

√ If you go to class, treat it like a study session.

√ Repetition is key.

√ Go to www.MedSchoolSurvivalKit.com/Reader to download a sample schedule.

√ Create your own schedule.

CH 3.
THE ART OF STUDYING

NOTE-TAKING

I remember when I used to think I was so effective at taking notes. I used to look at the slides, then write down exactly what the slides said in my notebook. Then read that over again. I did that for EVERY single slide. Then I realized I'd be spending hours re-writing the same things over and over again.

Note taking is an extremely important skill! If you try to write down and recreate every single lecture like you did in undergrad, you will not have enough time in the day to go over the information. You can spend hours talking beautiful, scrumptious, delicious, edible, perfect notes but then you end up rewriting the book again which is ultimately a huge waste of time.

When you are going through a powerpoint/ lecture, only take notes on topics that you do not understand.	**When you read a topic come up with your own notes and explain things in your own words. As you reword it, you will be more likely to remember that information.**

Pro Tip: If you want to crush exams, find and study with people who score high on exams. It can be a good way for you learn and a way for them to solidify information. Approach them with the "I'm trying to get on your level / I'm the grasshopper and I'm trying to learn from you Obi-Wan Kenobi" attitude. Make them feel good about themselves and they will be more eager to work with you.

Another key to note taking is to create your own story. One of my classmates who was very successful in school, I mean smart as bananas (AOA honor society, matched into Emergency Medicine), drew pictures to study. When she took notes, she made her own pictures of all the different diseases, or how different processes worked. Therefore, she was using the creative part of her brain to remember things and make things stick. See some examples on the next page.

You don't have to be a professional artist to draw things out. She made her own story and crafted her own images. This made studying somewhat fun. The program Sketchy Medical does a great job of incorporating this, which is a reason why they are so widely popular. (I'll get into those sources in a later chapter.)

HYPERCALCEMIA CAUSES

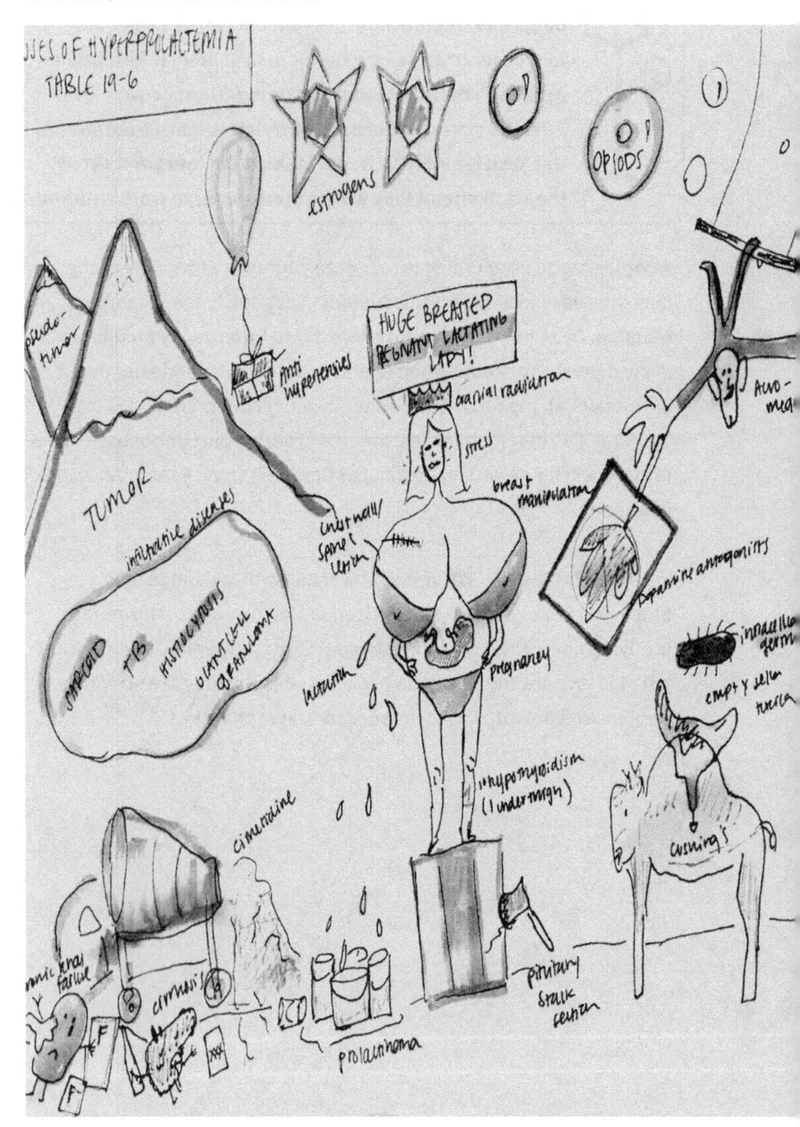

HEPATIC ENCEPHALOPATHY

Pictures courtesy of Agnieszka Gaertig, M.D.

There are different programs/apps that you can also use to help out with note-taking. Below I'll list some note-taking applications that can help you out.

Onenote	It's a program that you can paste PowerPoint's on to and write notes over them (which is especially helpful if you have a touchscreen). It's great because you can organize your notes into sections and have everything in one place.
Evernote	It is a free program where you can type and organize your notes as well as checklists, planning, etc. You can also sync your notes through your email so you can access them from other computers. There is a whole list of things that Evernote can do. There is a free and Premium version.
Supernote app	It's an app you can download onto your iPhone/tablet that can record lectures and you can take notes in the app too. You can go to a park and scroll through your phone and study without having to bring your books.
Mind42	It's a free app that you can use to make your own mind maps. It's a great way of organizing your own thoughts.

MEMORIZATION

There will be times where you just have to undergo brute force memorization. Everybody has different ways of doing things and memorizing information. Below are some tips to help you memorize information.

NOTECARDS

I personally hate notecards and can't stand using them, but some people love them. For those of you that do love them, many people use **Anki flashcard decks**. It's a good source to use because you can make your own flashcard deck, but there are also other flashcards that may already be made that you can use. If you are weak on a subject it will show more of that flashcard and if you are strong on a subject it will show less of that flashcard. You can also share flashcard decks between classmates. There are plenty of decks already made online.

STORYTELLING / PICTURES

A great way to memorize/understand information is to make it personal and create a visual story in your mind. Use places that you are familiar with (such as your car, room, or house) and incorporate the facts that you are trying to learn into it. The more extravagant and outlandish you make the facts that you are trying to learn in your story, the easier they are to remember.

Let me give you an example of using storytelling to memorize facts:

Topic	Symptoms/ Presentation	Pathology behind it	Labs
Takayasu arteritis	Usually Asian females < 40 years old. "Pulseless disease" (weak upper extremity pulses), fever, night sweats, myalgias, skin nodules, ocular disturbances)	Granulomatous thickening and narrowing of aortic arch + proximal great vessels	Inc ESR (Erythrocyte Sedimentation Rate), treat with steroids

Quick Story: Close your eyes and imagine in your mind that it's midnight and you're super hungry. You went to your local **Asian** food place, **Takayasu chicken**, to order some food and you can smell the aroma of food in the air. Your Asian female friend is there working behind the counter, but she looks different. Her lower body looks normal but her **upper body looks small and lifeless, barely moving her fingers** (weak upper extremity pulses). She screams "Who is there!" as she's **blinking a thousand** times (ocular disturbances).

You are like "What's going on here?" It's **pitch black outside**. You turn around and you look up at her forehead. She's **dripping beads of sweat onto the counter** (night sweats), **grabbing her arm in pain** (myalgias), and there is a **huge red skin nodule on the back of her arm**. The nodule is all crusty and red and you point to it in disgust (skin nodules).

You are like "What is going on?", but you are hungry so you look down to grab the grainy candy cane shaped pencil to fill out the paper to order. You feel the **grainy pencil** in your hand. It has some abnormally thin and thick portions (granulomatous thickening of the aortic arch). You pick the **first thing on the menu** (proximal vessels). She gives you some **ESR sauce** to put on your food right away (inc ESR). Then a **big, Hulk Hogan looking muscle guy** comes in with a huge needle and sticks your friend in her shoulder and she turns back to normal (treat with steroids).

Now, you can think back in your memory to all the cues: Asian female, small upper body/fingers barely moving- "pulseless upper extremity", dripping sweat on forehead + pitch black outside (fever + night sweats), grabbing her arm in pain (myalgias), crusty red disgusting nodule (nodules), thick + thin grainy candy cane pencil (granulomatous aortic arch thickening), ESR sauce (inc ESR), and big steroid guy (treat with steroids).

All you have to do is picture the scene in your head to remember the details. It may take you a minute to come up with your own story, but it can be easier to remember afterward. This tactic can work for virtually anything.

QUESTIONS

Now, one of the biggest and most important things that I wish I knew earlier on in medical school is the importance of doing practice questions. If there's anything out of this chapter, or out of this book, that you need to understand it is to do **practice questions. Do them early!**

I remember I was a gung-ho medical student at first, studying the material all week and I thought I had the information down pat. I knew everything on the slides. Then, I started to do some practice questions and I only got 50% correct. "What's going on here?!" I told myself. It wasn't until my second year of medical school that I realized questions force you to apply your knowledge. When you do a question, you get to find out if you really understand the information, how to apply it, and how it interconnects with different systems.

I tended to do questions **BEFORE** I read the material (everybody does it differently), but here is why I did it that way. When I saw the questions first, I got most of them wrong. I mean I'd be lucky if I got 20% right. So don't worry about getting them right. By doing it this way, I had a chance to see how the question writers can phrase the material and how they wanted me to apply the knowledge that I would soon learn.

So now, when I'm reading through the chapter and learning the information, I am processing it in the sense of, "Oh, I see how you can apply this concept to "x" and "I see this is how they can ask this in a question," because I've already seen some of the questions that I did before I started reading.

Here are two examples of how bodies of information can be applied to questions below:

1. Information: The major nerves that continue from the arm into the forearm include the radial, median, and ulnar nerves. These nerves provide sensation and control to the forearm muscles that move the wrist and the hand. The dorsal (posterior) aspect of the forearm is supplied by the radial nerve which controls the extensor muscles of the forearm. The volar (anterior) aspect of the forearm is supplied by the median and ulnar nerves which control the flexor muscles of the forearm and the intrinsic muscles in the hands and fingers. The nerves then continue to the hand where they branch off and form a network of fibers.

Question being asked:
A 28 year old male comes into the emergency room after being in a bar fight where he was stabbed in the back of his forearm with a knife. He complains of weakness in his hand and wrist and it is later found out that the knife severed a part of his radial nerve. Which of the following was this patient's most likely complaint?

A. Difficulty making a fist
B. Wrist drop
C. Trouble crossing fingers
D. Carpal Tunnel Syndrome
E. Severe pain on back of hand

What the question forces you to do is apply the knowledge that the radial nerve supplies the wrist and forearm extensors and it makes you think of what the clinical outcome would be. It also forces you to know the muscles groups involved with certain hand movements.

A- is incorrect. Making a fist would take mostly wrist flexors which would use the median/ulnar nerve. Some part of the extensor muscles are used in making a complete fist but there is a better answer.

C- is incorrect. The crossing of fingers is controlled by the deep hand muscles, mostly supplied by the ulnar nerves.

D- is incorrect. This is due to compression on the median nerve.

E- is incorrect. Although it is in the same sensory area as the radial nerve, the radial nerve is severed. The lesion also occurred at the forearm, so it'd be less likely to have severe pain in your hand.

B- is correct. Loss of wrist extension will lead to wrist drop.

Another Example:

2. Information: There are 3 parts to the small intestine. The duodenum, jejunum, and ileum.

Iron is absorbed in the duodenum, folate is absorbed in the small bowel (mostly jejunum), and B12 is absorbed in the terminal ileum along with bile salts.

Question: A 34-year-old male with Crohn's disease comes to your office complaining of severe abdominal pain and diarrhea. He is diagnosed with a fistula formation and has to undergo resection of his terminal ileum. Which of the following is a symptom that this patient is likely to have 2 years later?

A. Cheilosis
B. Burning sensation in their limbs bilaterally
C. Weakness and loss of sensation in their lower limbs bilaterally
D. Unrecognizable speech and memory problems
E. Dermatitis

Again, to answer this question correctly, you would have had to know #1 The different sections of the small bowel, #2 What substances are absorbed there, and #3 What a deficiency in that substance would appear like clinically. Therefore, once you know how you will need to apply the information that you will be learning, when you study it, you will be able to view the material through those lenses.

In case you were wondering, the answer to the question is C (the symptoms are caused by B12 deficiency). A, Cheilosis, is seen with different vitamin deficiencies and is nonspecific, B is seen in B5 deficiency, D is B1 deficiency, and E is a general symptom that can be seen in Zinc deficiency along with a myriad of conditions.

After seeing questions, when you start to review the material you will begin to make certain connections that you wouldn't have known to make before. So, however you decide to do your questions, the bottom line is to **DO PRACTICE QUESTIONS** to make sure you not only know the information but that you also know how to apply it. Do practice tests, question books, etc.

HOW MANY QUESTIONS SHOULD YOU DO?

Do as many as it takes for you to understand the material and score 90%+ consistently. I promise you, if you do very well on questions, you will do very well on exams.

SOURCES

Now let's talk about sources. What should we use? Should you just be reading a book 24/7? Should you just be listening to audios? Should you be watching videos? I personally think you should use all your senses when you're studying information. That being said, you should be reading, you should be listening to audios, and you should be watching videos on YouTube. Do it all. Hearing and seeing information about the same topic from different sources can help you remember it better! Sometimes you just get tired of reading.

Let's quickly touch on books. I had books in school, but these days there are so many PDFs that are available that have the exact same information. I can count on my hands how many actual hard copy books that I used. It's up to personal preference on what you choose to do. Just know that you may not have to go book crazy and spend thousands of dollars on books right away but be aware that there are certain books which you should always have a hard copy of.

Now, for each individual topic, or each individual class, I highlight some of the good YouTube channels and sources that you can use in order to help you understand the topic in the future chapters.

Pro Tip: I've found that a common trait in high achieving med students is watching videos on 2x the speed. At first, it will be hard to catch on but you get used to it.

KEY CHAPTER TAKEAWAY POINTS

√ Do practice questions. Do them early. It's the best way to test a concept.

√ Do questions.

√ Did I mention doing practice questions?

√ Anki flashcard decks to help memorization.

√ Onenote, Evernote, Powerpoint, Mind42 - Note-taking software.

√ What's the presentation for Takayasu Arteritis? Which marker is elevated? How do you treat it?

√ Watch videos on 2x speed.

√ Study with the smart kids.

CH 4.
STUDY ENVIRONMENT

Woohoo! You just read all of that. Stop for a second and pat yourself on the back. That was a lot of information in the previous chapter! Let's talk about where you study and the advantages/disadvantages to them.

SETTING UP YOUR ENVIRONMENT

So, you just got through with a full day of class and then afterwards went to get a workout in. Now it's time to go ahead and get some good ol' fashioned studying in. We all know studying will take up some time, but having the right study spot can make all of the difference as to how effective you can be in your allotted time.

Now, where should you study?

The places that you choose to study can play a tremendous role in your effectiveness and the amount of work you get done. During the school year, you should have certain places that you know are just for studying purposes only.

Should you study at home, in a library, in a coffee shop, or in the park? Studying at a location other than your home can work to your advantage, and here is why. You get used to studying outside of your home so when you get home your brain is not in study mode, it's in relax/other mode. You are training yourself to compartmentalize and to get work done in certain places. It can be the library, Starbucks, Uncle Joe's house, the club, or wherever you feel you will get the most work done.

This sets it up so that when you are in your designated study places your mind already knows that it needs to focus. In a sense, you are conditioning yourself while setting up good study habits. You can also do this at home, if you prefer, by having a designated study area. It can be a desk/table/hammock that you use for studying, and you can have your setup however you want it. Below are some of the advantages/disadvantages for studying at different areas.

STUDYING AT HOME

When I first started out in medical school, I used to study at home all of the time. Then, after awhile, I got bored and wanted to switch it up to another place. I returned to studying at home when I was studying for my STEP 1 exam. I think studying at home can be effective if you have an area that you know is for studying.

PROS

- Comfortable environment
- Nap when you want
- Food nearby
- Close to family/significant other
- You can have designated study area

CONS

- It can be too comfortable -> no work done
- Family/Spouse distractions
- You may get stuck in the YouTube black hole watching videos for hours

COFFEE SHOP

Personally, for my pre-clinical years, I found this to be very effective at certain times. The times where I needed to actually get work done and focus, I went to my local Starbucks. My thought process behind it was that I would HAVE to get work done here because I have nothing else to do. The internet connection would be too slow to stream movies/things that I wanted to do. I would put my earbuds in and get to work. I would also recommend a coffee shop because there is a little more commotion going on in the background.

Now, you're probably wondering why would I say that. I'm talking about the background movement, where every so often you will have to scoot your chair up in order to let somebody by, or you may see somebody you know and speak for a quick minute. The reason that I find this to be a good thing is that you will learn how to concentrate when there are a moderate amount of distractions. You will learn how to focus: from focusing on one thing, getting easily distracted, then focusing right back in, which will become a useful skill to have for your clinical years when you are in a hospital for the majority of the time. But we will get to that a little later.

PROS

- Learn to concentrate with distractions
- Nothing else to do but study

CONS

- You may have to buy a frappuccino
- It can get too social leading to no work done

LIBRARY

Studying in a library can also be good if you are concentrating and getting work done. It (generally) is a quieter environment and most people are there to study.

PROS

- Always a great place to study
- Optimized for studying
- Central location to meet classmates/group study

- You can consult classmates easily to help you understand topics
- Depending on your school, there may be free food at places in the school

CONS

- It can become social quickly if you're just chatting with friends

Also don't be afraid to switch it up sometimes for a little variety. Study in a park, on the plane, in a car on a road trip, and in the mountains. There are countless places where you can get work done.

GETTING IN THE ZONE

Sometimes you can get distracted and need help getting in the zone. There are plenty of ways to get around it. You can YouTube "white noise" or "jazz instrumentals" that can give you some background music. I also found myself getting distracted by going to different websites when I was supposed to be getting work done. I found some useful applications that you can use to keep you on track:

- **StayFocusd**
- **Freedom**
- **Cold Turkey**

SOLO GROUP VS STUDY GROUP?

I am a big promoter of using study groups, however, it has to be at the right time. There are different levels of understanding knowledge and information that should be met before you study in a group. Studying in a group when you are first learning the material is something that I would not recommend. I recommend being about 70-80% comfortable with the material before you start to study in a group.

GROUP STUDYING: THE RIGHT VS WRONG WAY

You should remember and know that this is a STUDY group, not a social group. What was originally supposed to be a "let's cover cardiac embryology" can quickly turn into a session of talking about who you all think are the most attractive people in your class. An hour and a half later you will the realize that you got no work done! (Not talking from experience here...or am I?)

Group studying is beneficial in many ways. Everybody has a different knowledge base and way of learning/processing information. Learning how other people look at problems or understand mechanisms works great. When working in groups you will also be using more senses, interacting with other people, and in some cases using emotions, which helps you remember certain information.

You may remember the name of that drug, or the side effect from a funny joke your friend made about it. Imagine making a gesture and saying trazoBONE with your friends...I bet you will remember what one of the side effects of the drug trazodone is then. (It's an erection)

Here are some go to tips for group studying:

√ **Have a clear objective of what you are going to go over for the day.**

Know that your objectives for the day are to cover cardiology: heart failure, myocardial infarctions, and cardiac drugs. Therefore, you have a measurable objective. You leave knowing that information and you can measure it the next day by doing a quick review.

√ **Put your phones on do not disturb mode.**

√ **Have people in your group go up and explain a concept entirely.**

I mean entirely, and question them about everything. What this does is it solidifies that you know the information. When you can explain a subject to other people, you are close to subject mastery. Being the person asking questions like WHY this mechanism, or WHAT an increase in that substance means, allows you to start looking at how different concepts can be asked on a test. It also answers any questions that you may not know.

On the contrary, asking questions gets you in the mind of the question writer and allows you to spin it and see how that topic can be approached. It also makes sure that the other person truly knows why something happens, and if you come to a question that you both can't answer you can look it up together.

Consider asking questions and being the one presenting the topic as a form of active learning

√ Set a time limit and roughly how long you will spend on each topic.

For example, when I was studying with my study partner for STEP 2, we knew that we would talk about Pediatrics for 2 hours, and then Ob-Gyn for the remaining 2 hours.

√ Do some questions on your own before you meet with the entire group.

That way, you have something to go off of and you have an idea of how some questions will be asked.

√ Have some fun with it.

Come up with crazy examples and enjoy yourself. The more outlandish stuff you guys do that stands out, the easier it will be to remember it. Which one of the following do you think that you would remember: you reading in a textbook that some of the symptoms of heart failure include shortness of breath, orthopnea, and increased jugular venous pressure, or that when your group covered heart failure, your classmate did an over the top demonstration, pretended like they were out of breath, and when they laid back, their breathing got even worse and then they turned their neck to the side you could see a bulging vein?

√ **Schedule some breaks if you need to.**

10-15 minute breaks where you guys just talk or chill out can be good too.

KEY CHAPTER TAKEAWAY POINTS

√ Have some areas set aside for studying specifically

√ Every once in a while, study somewhere new

√ Study Group does not equal Social Group time

√ Study in a group once you are 70-80% comfortable with the material

√ Applications to help you get and stay in the zone- Stay Focusd, Cold Turkey, freedom

CH 5.
FIRST-YEAR

Good ole first year. I remember those days. This is the year when you adopt your study habits and you figure out what works for you. I remember I was juggling a startup app while starting medical school. I would go to class, then go to a startup meeting to pitch ideas, work on marketing during lunch, then go back to school for lab, and then go home and study for the night. I remember the smell of formaldehyde in the gross anatomy and having to dissect male genitals-I was hurting on the inside that day!

This chapter is going to be quick points and tips on how to approach different subjects and different sources that most people found helpful for mastering the topic.

GOOD RESOURCES FOR FIRST YEAR:

In general:

Dr. Najeeb's lectures are great for physiology and biochemistry. He has free videos on YouTube that are great though some are shortened versions. He also has a website where students can get a lifetime membership and get access to all of his videos. Students that get his lifetime membership often say that it's a worthwhile investment.

HISTOLOGY

√ WashingtonDeceit YouTube Page

He has short videos that you can use for a quick review and they normally hit most of the high points needed.

√ Book- Histology & Cell Biology: Examination for Board Review

A book that has material and also practice questions to test your knowledge. It helps for your in-house exams as well as your board exams.

ANATOMY

A lot of anatomy is memorization, but understanding where different structures are in relation to one another is key. Also, nerve/muscle distribution and what would happen if a nerve is injured is good information to know. Drawing out the anatomy on a piece of paper can help you learn it too.

Awesome anatomy sources:

√ The Anatomy Zone YouTube Channel

He uses an animation model and goes through anatomy, the videos are about 10-15 minutes long. They are pretty helpful.

 **Sapiens Medicus MX YouTube Channel**

Great short videos to watch before anatomy lab. It's a cadaver dissection and they hit most of the high points needed for gross anatomy lab.

ACLANDS ANATOMY VIDEOS

These videos tend to be on the longer side and his examples are on a human cadaver. He goes into great detail and goes through bony anatomy, muscles, nerves, arteries, and veins. Watch on 2x the speed. You can search in YouTube and the part of the body and the videos will come up. I used these videos to brush up on anatomy before starting residency.

QUESTION BOOKS:

 **Lippincott's Illustrated Q&A Review of Anatomy and Embryology**

Great question book.

BIOCHEMISTRY

A lot of biochemistry is straight memorization.

 **Doctors in Training**

They have videos that prepare you for STEP 1, so some of the information may not be needed for your first-year material, but nonetheless, their biochemistry videos are good. They use mnemonics to remember certain information which works well.

√ Dr. Najeeb

Great source as mentioned before. Students say they remember his information long after learning the subject in class (which is awesome for STEP 1).

PHYSIOLOGY

Physiology is one of the most important, if not the most important, class that you should have a clear understanding of. This class is the foundation of medical school. Once you understand (not memorize) how the organ systems properly work then you will be able to reason out what would happen if one of the systems goes wrong.

I suggest approaching physiology from understanding the big picture first, then focusing down on the tiny details. Critically think through everything. For example, if your heart rate goes up then what would be the response to the peripheral vessels and WHY? The most important question to ask yourself when learning physiology is WHY? Why does the heart dilate? Why do the arteries constrict? Why? - Ask yourself (and your classmates) "why" at least 5 times on whatever topic you are talking about until you understand it all the way down to the cellular level.

CARDIOLOGY

Know the heart & functions, cause & effects, understanding afterload, preload, and EF (all important).

GASTROENTEROLOGY

Understand how each part of the bowel functions, the cells and their products, markers such as amylase and lipase, and the functions of all of the different tract organs.

EMBRYOLOGY

Learning embryology can help connect the dots with anatomy and physiology. Duke has a great site that I used to help supplement my embryology lectures. Google "Duke Embryology" and it's typically the first link.

PULMONOLOGY

Know how the lungs work. *Know how to interpret the pulmonary function graphs* (The graphs with the Residual Volume, FRC, TV, etc... You will learn what I'm talking about).

NEUROLOGY/NEUROANATOMY

It's all about the neural pathways and understanding what happens when a certain pathway is severed. I found DIT videos to be gold with this because they go through it in video form and you can follow the pathways from the brainstem to the spinal cord. Find some forms you can print out, fill out, and color in pathways. Dr. Najeeb has excellent videos as well.

PHYSIOLOGY SOURCES

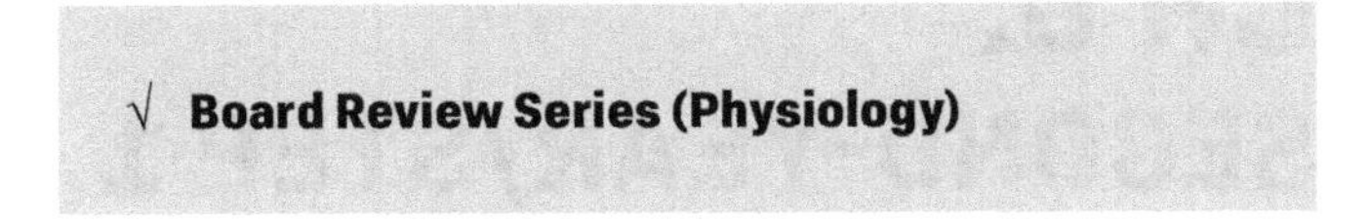

√ **Board Review Series (Physiology)**

A great book source to use to supplement what you are doing in class.

√ **Guyton and Hall Physiology Review**

We spoke about the importance of doing questions, so you should have a good physiology question book to test your knowledge. This book has good questions to help prepare you for your exam.

KEY CHAPTER TAKEAWAY POINTS

√ **Honestly, try to learn as much as you can about every topic.**

CH 6.
SECOND-YEAR/STEP 1

HOW TO GET A 250 ON STEP 1

So let's talk about the STEP 1 exam a.k.a. THE GREAT EQUALIZER. It is arguably the most important test of your medical school career. STEP 1 has been called the great equalizer because medical schools have different ways of grading their students. Some schools have the A, B, C, D, F system, some have the pass/fail system, and others have an honors based system. The STEP 1 exam objectively puts everybody on the same playing field, and it puts you up against the entire nation so you can see which percentile you stand in.

This is why residency programs use this score as their first cutoff. Doing great on STEP 1 is going to open doors as far as what specialty you choose. Certain specialties have different STEP 1 averages (you can check them out by going to NRMP.org). It's a lot easier to get into the residency program and specialty of your choice if you scored a 255 on your STEP 1 exam than if you have a 200, and you're trying to match into let's say neurosurgery, dermatology, orthopedic surgery- some of the more competitive specialties.

THE SETUP

This exam takes place at a Prometric Testing Center (you can go to usmle.org to find one). They are located all over the United States.

It's an 8 HOUR exam. There are seven sections that consist of 40 questions per section with an hour of break time. Each section is an hour long. (as of 2018)

If you finish your questions before the hour, the time that you don't use for that section gets added to your break time. You can take as many breaks as you want in between each of the sections. Each person is also assigned a locker so you can bring your notebooks and snacks. Some centers are cold, so I'd bring a jacket too.

QUESTION BANKS

Now if you didn't read my previous chapter on studying effectively, you may have skipped over one of the most important sections in this book.

The power of **QUESTIONS**.

You NEED to do them. It's a MUST!!!!

Now imagine if you just went through your second year of med school, never did any practice questions, and walked right into taking the STEP 1 exam. How successful do you think you would be? Unless you have a Jimmy Neutron brain or two fairly oddparents to grant you your STEP 1 wishes, I wouldn't recommend that.

There are a lot of questions banks out there that help you learn the material, but undoubtedly the best question bank to use, and that you will hear most people have used, is the **UWorld USMLE Test Prep** question bank.

It covers the topics that are on the actual exam. The question format appears exactly like the format of the questions on the STEP 1 exam. This helps you to get used to the functionality and format of the

STEP 1 exam. **So for the rest of this chapter, when I talk about doing questions, I am only referring to USMLE UWorld.**

UWORLD - WHEN TO START + HOW TO USE

When you go into second-year/your step year, you should have your STEP 1 starter kit ready. The STEP 1 starter kit consists of your:

- *First Aid for the USMLE STEP 1 Book*
- Your personal notebook
- UWorld subscription

Those are the bare essentials you need to pass the exam. I'll get into other resources later.

The best time to start doing UWorld questions is when you are covering the subject in class. As soon as we started our cardiac unit, I started doing my cardiac UWorld questions. My goal was to always have all of the UWorld questions in the subject DONE by the time we were done with that subject.

That meant not only having the pathology and pathophysiology sections of cardiology done, but the biostatistics, microbiology, immunology, and all of the other subsections done as well. This way, by the time you are done with the school year and before your designated study period, you are nearly done going through UWorld questions for the first time.

AKA the 1st pass

HOW MANY TIMES SHOULD YOU GO THROUGH UWORLD?

The amount of times you want to get through UWorld ideally is at least two times before you take the exam. The first time would be throughout the school year along with your classes and the second time would be while you are in your designated study period.

Some go through UWorld a third time, but most people say that when they did that, they would literally just remember the question and automatically know the answer from memory and get the question right. It makes you feel all tingly inside because you score 100% almost every time, but you aren't getting any real studying in.

Also, during your first pass, I'd recommend doing your questions by section. For example: Doing all of the cardiac pathology questions, then pharmacology, etc. That way you really learn a topic before you move on to the next, and your personal notebook will be organized. On your second pass, I would recommend doing the questions in a random order since the test will be in a random order.

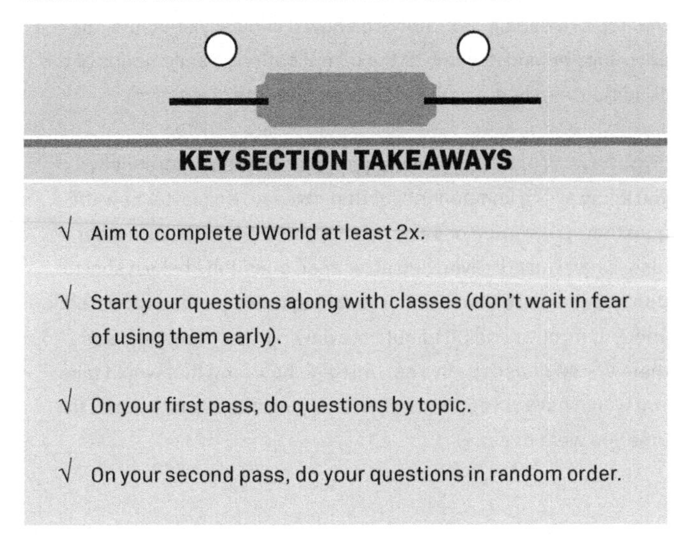

KEY SECTION TAKEAWAYS

√ Aim to complete UWorld at least 2x.

√ Start your questions along with classes (don't wait in fear of using them early).

√ On your first pass, do questions by topic.

√ On your second pass, do your questions in random order.

HOW TO USE UWORLD

At one point, I interviewed 3 of my high achieving colleagues who got a 250+ on the STEP 1 exam and we spoke about their mindset, how they approached questions, and how they used UWorld. I actually turned it into a two-part podcast episode (www.IamDrCole.com/step1pt1).

I bring that up because they all used similar tactics when approaching their STEP 1 exam and how they used questions.

When you go through UWorld, I recommend you either have a notebook that is completely separate and only used for STEP 1 studying that you take notes in, or you annotate and take notes in First Aid. When you go through UWorld questions, take notes **regardless of whether you get a question right OR wrong**. Do that at least for the first pass going through UWorld.

When you complete a question, there will be the basic topic/concept that the question is trying to cover. You should review all parts of that topic. Meaning, take notes on how it clinically presents, the pathology behind it, some of the complications/associations of the condition, and how you diagnose and treat the disease.

If you have all of this information for a topic, then theoretically you know all the components of that disease. No matter how the question is reworded or switched up, you will be able to answer it. Also, when you are reviewing after each question, make it short. **Don't spend more than 5 minutes taking notes per question**. Think about it, if you spend 30 minutes reviewing each question, and there are 40 questions in a set, imagine how long that would take. You would have scraggly grey hairs coming out of your ears by the time you were done.

So for example, if you get a question on Gout, your notebook note would look like this:

GOUT	
Presentation:	Acute swollen, painful joint. Tophi
Pathology:	precipitation of Urate crystals, needle-shaped - birefringent under polarized light
Complications/ Associations:	Alcohol use, Tumor Lysis Syndrome, Lesch-Nyhan syndrome
Diagnose(Dx)/ Treatment(Tx):	Dx- Aspiration. Tx- Acute-NSAIDs, steroids, colchicine, Chronic (preventive) - Allopurinol, febuxostat (XO inhibitors)

Another example:

CARDIAC TAMPONADE	
Pres:	Beck's triad (Hypotension, distended neck veins, distant heart sounds), +/- pulsus paradoxus
Path:	Compression of heart by fluid
Compl/ Assoc:	Free wall rupture, trauma, radiation therapy, infection
(Dx)/(Tx):	Equal pressure in all 4 chambers, EKG-low voltage QRS complex

By the end of your first pass through UWorld you should have over a thousand of these in your notebook (or annotated in First Aid if you'd rather do that).

In the **first 10/15 minutes** of your daily studying, GO OVER YOUR NOTEBOOK THAT YOU'VE WRITTEN. It's like you are seeing/doing the question again since you are reviewing it. If you start this early and are constantly reviewing the notebook, the more information you will know and the easier it will be for you. You will be a beast flying through questions.

QUESTIONS THAT YOU GET RIGHT

Now when I got questions right I rated them in three categories:

1- I knew that like the back of my hand, 2- I kind of knew that, And 3- I have no idea what this is or how I got it right. UWorld gives you the function to mark questions, so mark the questions that you got right but weren't 100% sure how you got it right (Category 2 & 3). The problems that you got wrong automatically go in the incorrect questions bank and you re-do those questions later on. This way, you can go back through your marked questions and unmark it when you get it right and you can do all of the questions you got incorrect before resetting the UWorld Qbank.

The bottom line is that no matter what, after EVERY SINGLE question, whether you get it right or wrong, go and read about the topic and learn it again (at least on your first go around).

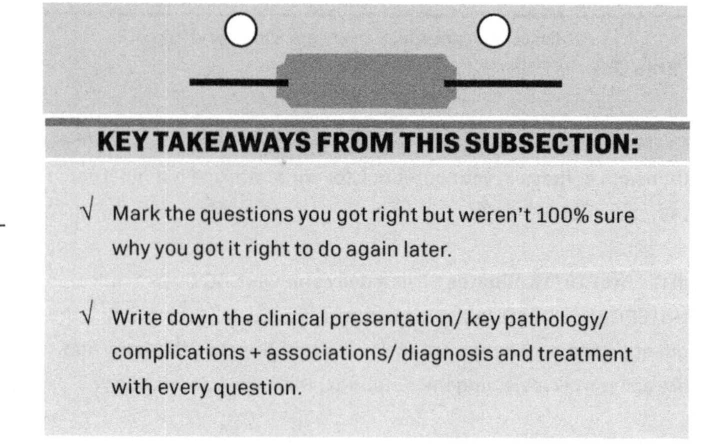

√ Have a separate notebook just for STEP 1 questions (or annotate in First Aid if you prefer).

√ Review your STEP 1 notebook the first 15 minutes of studying every day.

ProTip: A friend of mine who just matched into Orthopaedic surgery organized topics by certain colors. If it was red, he definitely had to review the information, blue - he kind of had to go over it, and green - he spent less time reviewing those concepts

Another suggestion on how you can approach the topics you decide to study is to divide the general topics into three categories:

1. I got this, no need to spend a lot of time studying it.
2. I once knew this pretty well but could benefit from review.
3. I never could learn this, never will, not going to waste time on it.

You would get the biggest bang for your buck by studying the things in category 2, so that's where you should put the bulk of your time in and only give a courtesy review to category 1, and look at category 3 right before the exam. What goes into each category will vary by person, but dividing it up like that will maximize the benefit of studying things they can get the most value from.

THE ANATOMY OF A QUESTION /HOW TO LOOK AT QUESTIONS

I recently became a writer for a STEP 1 question bank. I believe understanding how questions are written and the goal behind a question can help you kill the test. They shared an article on question writing with us and I wanted to share with you some of what I got from it. Here are some high points on STEP 1 questions:

STEP 1 QUESTIONS DON'T TEST FACTS, THEY TEST THE APPLICATION OF CLINICAL KNOWLEDGE.

- Ex: Identify the cause (drug, infection)
- Associated findings: (physical exam, labs)
- Treatment

EACH QUESTION FOCUSES ON ONE IMPORTANT CONCEPT.

- The best incorrect answers are based on common misconceptions and mistakes.
- A successful test taker should be able to answer the question without looking at the answers.

TYPICALLY QUESTIONS HAVE THIS TYPE OF A FORMAT:

- Age and gender (34-year-old male)
- Site of Care (Emergency Department)
- Chief Complaint (presents with headache)
- HPI
- Relevant PMH, PSHx, FHx, and SH (hypertension, smoking)
- Relevant (wheezes in lungs)
- Diagnostic/laboratory studies
- Tx, follow-up, clinical course, subsequent findings

Each of those bullet points in the question format gives you a valuable piece of information. There are some conditions that are more likely to present as a 65 y/o male in the emergency department rather than a 19 y/o female at the clinic.

Heart disease may be more common in a 65 y/o. The question many times sets you up and gives you clues as to what you should be expecting. Here's an example: A 70 y/o male with a history of smoking 2 packs of cigarettes per day comes to the emergency department due to shortness of breath. If you had to choose, which one would be first on the list of your possible diagnosis: Asthma or Chronic Obstructive Pulmonary Disease, which one would you think based off of the question stem alone? Exactly.

... The answer is Chronic Obstructive Pulmonary Disease by the way.

APPROACHING THE QUESTIONS:

I remember reading questions, straining to get through what seemed like the length of a personal statement from J.K. Rowling, and getting to the end of the question only to have it ask me, "what is the side effect of verapamil?" I wanted to turn the whole table over. Have you ever seen those memes of the frustrated guy? That was me.

I wasted my precious time formulating a list of diagnoses for what I thought the problem was and possible solutions for each diagnosis all to get to the bottom of the question and find out that I just needed to answer what the side effect of a medication was.

This is why I (and other high performing students) generally approach a question by taking a quick glance at the last sentence of the question and the answer choices. From there you will get a sense of what the question will be asking about. Then as you read through the question you want to formulate what you think the diagnosis is. Let's work through a couple questions that I wrote using the following method:

1. Read the **last sentence and answer choices** to get an idea what the question is saying.
2. Read through the question stem and start to formulate your top diagnoses with each sentence.
3. Figure out what the question is really asking you.

QUESTION 1:

An 18-year-old male comes to the office due to left knee pain for 3 weeks. He has a 2-year history of knee pain and is an active wrestler on the wrestling team. He denies any fevers, weakness, numbness, or tingling in his lower extremities. On physical examination, his knee appears swollen and slightly tender to touch. The knee is not warm to the touch. Which of the following conditions is most likely responsible for this patient's findings?

A. Torn Anterior Cruciate Ligament
B. Septic Arthritis
C. Bakers Cyst
D. Prepatellar bursitis
E. Gout

#1- Reading last sentence + answer choices = This question is asking for a diagnosis. The answer choices have to do with the musculoskeletal system. So you know that physical exam findings may be an important part of the question.

#2- An **18-year-old** male comes to the office due to **left knee pain** for **3 weeks**.

From here, A is lower on the differential as an ACL tear would likely present before 3. B is a possible answer, as is C and D. E is possible but typically presents in the distal extremities. Gout can present in the knee though so it's still a valid option.

He has a **2-year history of knee pain** and is an **active wrestler** on the wrestling team.

This line gives you the duration and also tells you that this patient is an avid wrestler (which is important). Wrestlers are on their knees a lot, which brings D higher up on the differential because prepatellar bursitis is common in patients with repetitive knee trauma.

A is even lower on the differential seeing as this patient has a 2-year history of knee pain. B is less likely as septic arthritis generally wouldn't take 2 years to present. C is a possible answer. E is still possible too even though it is lower.

He denies any fevers, weakness, numbness, or tingling in his lower extremities.

- Lack of fevers makes septic arthritis less likely.

On physical examination, his **knee appears swollen** and **mild tenderness to touch**. The knee is **not warm to the touch**.

- Further makes septic arthritis less likely.

#3- Summary- We have an active 18 y/o wrestler with chronic knee pain & swelling. The question is asking what the diagnosis is.

D - Prepatellar bursitis is the most likely answer. It is a common condition in patients who have repetitive knee trauma.

Pro Tip: STEP 1 won't say that they have repetitive knee trauma but they will make you infer it. They will say things like this patient is a wrestler or a plumber.

QUESTION #2:

A 40-year-old female with rheumatoid arthritis comes to the emergency department due to lightheadedness. The patient is also in her second month of radiation therapy for cancer treatment. For the past week, she has also had a low energy level. Otherwise, her medical history is insignificant. The patient's temperature is 37 C (98.6 F), blood pressure is 80/55 mm Hg, and her pulse is 110 and regular. Upon physical examination, her lungs are clear to auscultation, but her heart sounds are distant and the jugular veins are distended. When she inspires her pulses becomes barely palpable. Which of the following will most likely be seen on cardiac electrocardiogram?

A. Electrical alterans
B. Widespread ST elevations
C. PR depressions
D. Mobitz type II AV block
E. No discreet P waves in between irregularly spaced QRS complexes

#1- The last sentence asks us to identify what will be seen on laboratory EKG findings for this patient. So we need to have knowledge of what the clinical diagnosis is in order to answer that question. We also know it is most likely a cardiac question.

#2 - A **40-year-old female** with **rheumatoid arthritis** comes to the emergency department due to **lightheadedness**.

- Nothing too specific yet to rule in/out diagnosis. Just a risk factor of RA.

The patient is also in her second month of **radiation therapy** for cancer treatment.

This was stated for a reason.

- For the past week, she has also had a low energy level. Otherwise, her medical history is insignificant.

The patient's temperature is 37 C (98.6 F), blood pressure is **80/55 mm Hg**, and her pulse is **110** and **regular**.

- The patient is hypotensive and slightly tachycardic.

Upon physical examination, her lungs are clear to auscultation, but her **heart sounds are distant** and the **jugular veins are distended**. When she **inspires her pulses becomes barely palpable**.

- Key pertinent physical exam findings of JVD, distant heart sounds, and pulsus paradoxus. We have been given what is known as Beck's triad in disguise (hypotension, JVD, distant heart sounds) which is pathognomonic for Cardiac tamponade. Another clue is also added in and you are given the fact that this patient has pulsus paradoxus.

#3 - Summary We have a 40 y/o female with lightheadedness, Becks triad, and pulsus paradoxus. She has cardiac tamponade. The question is really asking: what is the EKG finding seen in Cardiac tamponade?

Answer. A - Electrical alterans is the main EKG finding seen in cardiac tamponade.

If you practice going through questions in this manner, you can get to what the question writers want you to know and get the question right!

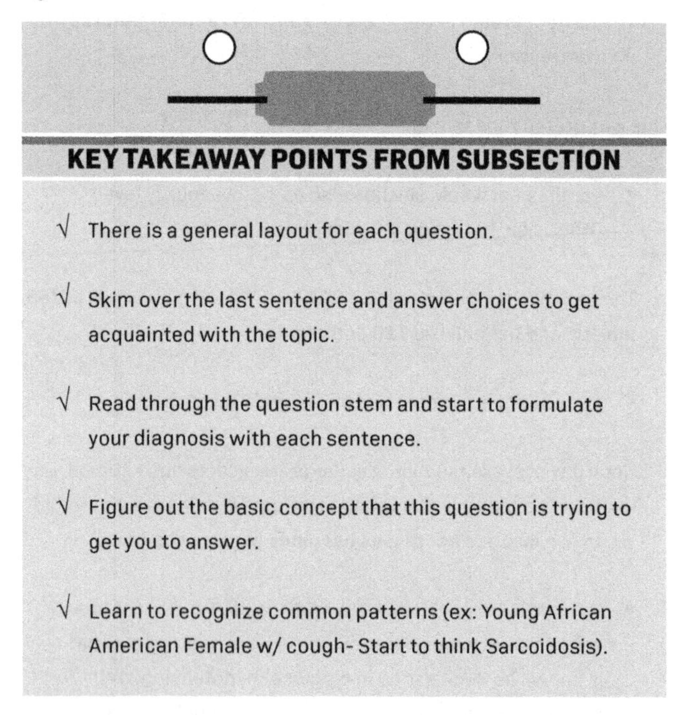

DESIGNATED STUDY PERIOD/PRACTICE EXAMS

SCHEDULING

Generally, most schools give you a period designated entirely for STEP 1 studying, and the amount of time they give you varies so you have to check that with your school. Some students say that they have been given a week to study and others were given 3 months to study. So there is a wide range. Those that were given a week to study generally had time during their school year to study.

Some schools also schedule their STEP 1 at different times. I have a friend that took her STEP 1 after her third year of medical school although, most students do it after their second year of medical school. Check with your institution about your date.

I suggest when it comes to STEP 1 studying that you go use a MACRO/MICRO approach, meaning know what you are going to cover over the week and know what you are going to cover on a day-by-day basis. I am normally not the type to put together a schedule, but for this test, you should make sure you cover all of your areas and execute.

I recommend that you take the first day of your designated study period to take a practice exam, then make your schedule according to how you score on the test. You should spend more time on the areas where you scored lower on the test versus the areas where you scored the highest.

√ **A quick note on practice exams, there are generally two that people use:**

NBME- Great resources to use for the test. They used to not give explanations but now they do. They also tend to be close to your actual score.

UWorld Self Assessments- There are two practice tests (in 2018). They look exactly like the test and they give you explanations. Generally, people say that your scores on here tend to be a bit inflated, but everybody is different. (My last UWorld self-assessment before my test was two points below my actual score).

I'd suggest doing **at least** 3 tests. One at the beginning, middle, and end of your study period before your review time. Some people do 4 tests, but doing 2 tests back to back to simulate sitting for 8/9 hours- is also not a bad idea.

The goal is to get through the UWorld Qbank at least two times before you take your STEP 1 exam.

ProTip: Get a study partner and take a practice test the same day as they do, so you both can go over the answers together out loud. Go through the answers the same day.

CREATING YOUR ACTUAL SCHEDULE

After you have taken your practice test on the FIRST day of your designated study period, you can do the following:

#1- Calculate the number of days from your designated study period to your test date.

#2- Determine how many days a week you want to study (some people take Sunday off).

#3- Determine how much review time you need (I suggest you spend anywhere from 10-15% of your study time reviewing).

#4- Create your daily schedule, giving yourself more time to review subjects that you are weaker on.

 # OF DAYS UNTIL TEST DAY **60**

SUNDAYS OFF? 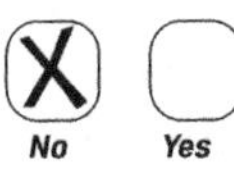 No [X] Yes [ ]

REVIEW TIME (10-15%) **10% = 6 days**

STUDY BREAKDOWN: **STUDY DAYS = 54 REVIEW DAYS = 6**

#OF PRACTICE TESTS: 3

SUBJECT COMFORTABILITY

	DO YOU EVEN LIFT BRO? (WEAK)	OK	STRONG	DAYS TO STUDY
CARDIO		✓		9
NEURO			✓	6
RESP	✓			12
G I	✓		✓	12
MSK				6
OTHER		✓		9

	Su	M	T	W	Th	F	S
WEEK 1	Practice test/ N	N	N	N	N	N	N
WEEK 2	GI	GI	GI	GI	GI	GI	GI
WEEK 3	GI	GI	GI	GI	C	C	R
WEEK 4	Practice test/ C	C	C	C	C	C	C
WEEK 5	R	R	R	R	R	R	R
WEEK 6	R	R	R	R	MSK	MSK	MSK
WEEK 7	MSK	MSK	MSK	0	0	0	0
WEEK 8	0	0	0	0	0	Practice test/ Review	Review
WEEK 9	Review	Review	Review	Review	Test day		

N = Neuro C= Cardio R= Resp MSK= Muskuloskeletal O= Other

During your normal study period, crank out questions, review your annotated First Aid/ STEP 1 notebook DAILY, and get it done. During your **review period (the 10% of your study period that you reserved)**, primarily focus on the sections that you are weaker on (based on the results from you practice test), but eventually review all of your information. Read through your First Aid book/STEP 1 notebook one more time.

A LITTLE MOTIVATION

This is your time to crank it out. Smash through UWorld questions, read up on questions you got wrong, and review those topics.
This is the time where you are not going to be known to the world. Deactivate your social media. You are going to be cranking out 10/14 hour days. There are going to be times where you will be tired, stressed, angry from missing questions, or even sad for whatever reason.

You are training for a world title fight right now. There is no time for distractions and no time to mess around. This is what you worked for; your first two years prepared you for the STEP 1 exam. Each lecture you've attended have been sit-ups, each question you have been doing is a push-up, each practice test you take in your school is a sparring class, and the big match is coming up. You can do it. You are only facing what other people have done.

The people that have scored crazy scores (250's & 260's) - what do they all have in common? They are human. If somebody else can do it, so can you. It's all about your will power. So what if you started off scoring a 210 on your first practice test? Go do something about it. How bad do you want it? Do you want to be able to choose what specialty you can do? This test has the opportunity to change your life and give you the lifestyle you have been dreaming of. Nothing comes easy.

You will look back after the test and say "I can't believe I did that," "I can't believe it's over," and "I'm glad it's done." This is not going to last forever. Take a short period of your life and go hard. Hit the books/laptops/whatever you do. Once a week take a day to chill and relax, then get right back at it. Get it done.

TOP RESOURCES FOR 2ND-YEAR/ STEP 1

First Aid for the USMLE STEP 1

This is by far the most common book used for Step 1 studying. This is a book you definitely need a hard copy of. Use it to go along with your classes and while you do UWorld questions. Many of my colleagues annotate and take notes in their First Aid book and it becomes their STEP 1 bible.

ProTip: At the back of the book there are a bunch of high yield facts that you can go over a couple days before your exam as a review. It's a great passive way of studying.

MICROBIOLOGY

The tiny critters that can cause a whirlwind of problems. Microbiology is a lot of memorization but is also a very important section. It's a good thing there is a resource that solves all of your problems. Hands down, **SketchyMedical** is the go-to source for Microbiology. I barely missed any microbiology questions because of this program.

SketchyMedical is a program that gives you a unique way to learn information. They create stories/videos and have visual cues to represent the types of bacteria there are, the clinical symptoms, and treatments as well. This not only helped me during STEP 1 studying but also throughout my 3rd year of medical school. To this day, I still remember microbiology facts because of Sketchy Micro.

About 95% of micro is covered by using Sketchy. The other 5% you can find in the UWorld question bank and First Aid for STEP 1.

PHARMACOLOGY

As Pablo Escobar would say, "¡Las drogas!" Also known as Memorization CENTRAL with a side of side effects (see what I did there?). Your goal in this class is to understand the mechanisms of different drugs, their interactions, and the side effects of each medication. **Especially the lethal side effects**!

Along with your **class lectures**, SketchyMedical came out with **SketchyPharm** which is a great resource to use as well. I still remember some of the sketches in my head and, no doubt, it helped me to remember all of those tedious little side effects. I remember that field of fluoroquinolones and that table with all of the delicious looking food on it.

Also, **Kaplan** has great videos that cover medications. The teacher does a fantastic job of walking you through the different types of drugs, when they are used, and some of the history behind the drugs which helps them to stick. You can listen to these in the car while you drive as well.

First Aid has pharmacology sections with each Organ System that covers high yield information.

PHARM

- SketchyMedical
- Your Class Lectures
- Kaplan Pharmacology Videos
- First Aid for USMLE STEP 1

PATHOLOGY

AKA just a ton of information. Pathology and pathophysiology make up the majority of the STEP 1 exam (60-70%) so understanding this down to the core is very important. In my class, we used to have 100 slide powerpoints per class and we had to know EVERY little detail on the slides because you never knew what would come up on the test.

The best and most used book for pathology is Robbins and Cotran Pathologic Basis of Disease. The good thing about buying the book is that you get a code which gives you access to their online case studies. These studies have a lot of histology and pathology slides that aid in learning pathology (it's a REALLY good source).

If you are a person that reads books, definitely read this book. Read what you are going to go over BEFORE class so that when you go to lecture, you can ask informed questions (going back to the chapter on the art of studying).

Pathoma is another great resource (along with the book). Pathoma is a video resource that most people use. I would suggest watching the videos on a specific topic before the lecture. It is a great resource to give you an overview of the material and he states the information in a way that helps you understand concepts versus simply memorizing facts.

If you purchase Pathoma, you will receive the videos plus a textbook that consists of all the points made in the videos. It helps with following along with the videos and gives you a resource to annotate. I wouldn't use it as your sole source, as it doesn't go into enough detail for exams.

The library at Utah also has a great site for pathology histology that is gold! Google "Utah pathology histology". Seriously, that site is gold!

PATHOLOGY

- Robbins
  Buy for access to their online case studies
- Pathoma
- First Aid

PATHOPHYSIOLOGY

What will help you understand pathophysiology is a rock solid understanding of physiology. Once you know how everything works (not memorize but understand the concepts), it is easy to figure out how an organ system or a process messing up will affect the whole body.

One specific source that I used was *Pathophysiology of Heart Disease* (Lilly). Cardiology is always going to be a big chunk of the STEP 1 exam and a concrete knowledge of how this organ system works will take you a long way.

BIOSTATISTICS

First Aid provides a QBank designated to BioStats. I highly recommend that you utilize this. BioStats questions are easy points to get on the exam. Use First Aid and memorize the equations and concepts. Don't miss out on these easy points. Most people usually save this to go over the week before the test.

HONORABLE MENTIONS

Many people use **Firecracker** as a passive way to study. It is a great source you can use to memorize facts. The good thing is that you can set it up so it gives you a number of flashcards/questions to go through per day. A colleague of mine used to wake up and do firecracker questions and go to bed using firecracker questions.

USMLERx is another question bank that some people use. I would recommend you go through UWorld first and use it as an adjunctive if you have time (or use it very early in your study process).

CH 7.
RESEARCH AND HOW TO GET PUBLISHED

WHY RESEARCH?

If you are looking to match into a competitive field, research is almost always necessary. Residency applications have an entire section for you to put in your research, your publications, abstracts, presentations, and etc. so it is safe to say that residency programs look at it.

Many residency programs need to have research projects to be accredited by the ACGME (Accreditation Council for Graduate Medical Education), so if you are a student who is interested in research it can be a plus for your application when you have some projects under your belt already. Research helps you stand out in a field of applicants, it deepens your knowledge of the scientific process, and it can help further the field of medicine. So let's touch on how you can get involved in research, how to write your paper, and how to get it published.

HOW TO GET INVOLVED IN RESEARCH

DECIDE WHAT KIND

First off, you should have an idea of what type of research you want to get involved in. Do you want to do bench work where you will be in a lab most of the time? Do you want to do clinical research/surgical/pharmaceutical? There are projects that take years to complete, and there are shorter projects and case studies you can write up and finish within months. What's your goal?

My goal was to get involved in something I was interested in and could PUBLISH. That way, I could make a contribution to the field of medicine as well as having something to put on my CV/application. It is important to note that before you start a project you should check with your attending/institution to see whether or not you need IRB approval.

Pro Tip: Continuously update your CV during medical school. Update it every time you attend a conference, make a presentation, receive an award, etc. It saves you a ton of time in the long run, especially when you are applying for residency and need to remember everything you have done. Without documentation it's only speculation!

WHAT TO SAY TO WHO

After you figure out what kind of research project you want to do, who do you talk to and what do you say? There are many ways to get involved in projects.

√ Ask attending physicians

Literally, go to attendings at your university/hospitals or at nearby residency programs and tell them that you are interested in research and are free to help out in any way you can. Offer to write the introduction, do a literature search, crunch data numbers, write up a case study, pull images, WHATEVER. You are a medical student who wants to lend a hand; get in where you can.

This worked for me. I was able to meet with an attending from a nearby residency program. I told him I was interested in the program and asked if he had any projects I could help out with. He paired me up with one of the residents (also another plus) and I was able to do a literature search, write part of the paper, and it ended up getting published with my name on the paper.

My friend and classmate Christian who matched into Family Medicine wanted to get involved with a trauma project. He simply asked his Trauma attending physician to help out and see if there was any way he could do something to get involved. He was presenting 2 months later and got published in the American Surgeons Journal.

√ Ask residents

This is overlooked. Many residency programs have a research minimum that the residents have to be involved with. Residents are super busy and in many cases would love to have a medical student there to help them out. Ask them if you can help find papers for them or do anything that they need. Plus, if this is a resident in your given field, it's a way to make a connection. Build a relationship and possibly make a mentor.

I did this with a resident that worked at the hospital I rotated through. I would volunteer to help out on weekends to get exposure to the field I was interested in and I asked him if there were any projects going on that I could help him out with.

He had a case study that he gave me the information for, told me to do some research to see if there were many reported cases like this one out there (there weren't), and said that I could write it up and be the first author on the paper. Put yourself out there.

√ Email academic departments (Thank you, Parth Patel, M.D. for this tip)

Look up a university/hospital in town that has research funding on the internet. Usually, each department has a research director/a clinical director. Email and approach them in a professional way to let them know that you want to invest your time and yield productive research work. (This conveys that you aren't looking to mess around and work on a project that will never get published).

Tell them you want to work with a mentor on a research project that is publishable and feasible to be completed within the next 6 months-1yr. Sometimes universities will have research meetings where the physicians are present. Ask the director if you can sit in on a meeting to observe and see the current projects that are being worked on. From there, work your way on towards a project!

√ Get involved in summer programs

Another great way to get involved in research between your first and second years of medical school is to get involved in a research program/internship where you will have the opportunity to get some research done. Sometimes the research you do may not be publishable, but you may be able to write up an abstract/prepare a poster presentation and present it at conferences and different meetings. That is a great way to meet people in your field and build relationships.

√ **Just email everybody**

This reminds me of a friend of mine that got involved in cancer research at the age of 17 when he was still in high school. His name is Keven Stonewall. I interviewed him for a podcast that I host, and he told me the story of when he literally looked up professors in different labs and just sent an email to everybody. He emailed more than 50 people. Most of them didn't reply or said no, but one person responded and said yes. From there, he was able to get his foot in the door and since then has gone on to make advancements in the field of cancer, be featured in magazines, be a TedX speaker, and is now starting his medical school journey.

WRITING THE PAPER

WHERE TO LOOK FOR ARTICLES

Most people use Pubmed.com to search for articles. Your school/library may give you access to Pubmed so check with them. If you don't have access, see if you know a resident. Many of them have access as well.

You can also find good articles in the journals within the field you are doing your research in. For example, in orthopaedics, the Journal of the American Academy of Orthopaedic Surgeons is a highly credible source to find good articles in that field. There are different reputations for different journals. You can generally ask your attending physician about the reputation of a specific journal that you are using for your source.

Another hack is that if you found an article that is on the topic of what you are researching, go to the bottom of the article, look at the articles they have cited, and look those up. It's a great way to find articles that speak about a similar topic.

WRITING YOUR PAPER

Great! You've found a place where you can fit in and help out, now it's time to write your paper. I'd suggest you make a timeline of when you want to get it done. I try to not take more than 3-4 weeks to have everything written up and sent to the attending/resident. This is your time to get work done. You made it this far so it's time you deliver. You don't want to be in the position to get involved in research and then mess it up by fooling around for 4 months and not get anything done.

Sit down and crank the paper out in a weekend if you can. Also, a great tip that will take you long in life is to **UNDERPROMISE AND OVERDELIVER**. If I KNOW I can finish the paper within a week, I will tell the attending/somebody else that I can have it done in two weeks. That way, when I turn it in a week early, I am on top of the game and I seem like a rockstar. Also, if anything does get messed up, it's a good thing I have an extra week to fix it.

Also, take initiative and write up the first draft of the paper if nobody has done so. That way you will be the first author on the paper. Any changes made after the first draft will just be edits. If you wrote part of the paper and/or did a literature search on the paper, make sure your name is on the paper. Get the credit you deserve.

When it comes to writing the paper I use Microsoft Word. A great program to help you manage your references is **Mendeley**. It's a software that you can use to help organize and manage your articles, cite your work using Word, and will automatically create a bibliography for you at the end of your paper. It also keeps the sources in order. There are folders that you can use to organize for each project you are working on and it's free!

Other software to help you manage and organize your references are Endnote ($250) and Papers for Mac ($70).

CHOOSING A JOURNAL TO SUBMIT TO

When choosing what journal to submit your article to, read through some of their titles in their last edition and see if your research will fit into that topic. If all of your research is on colon cancer I doubt your paper will get submitted into a pediatric cardiology journal. Also, find out the reputation of the journal and see if you can find their articles through Pubmed.

PRESENTING YOUR RESEARCH

Even if you don't get a publication out of your research, you still have the option to present what you have worked on at different conferences. You can present your abstract/poster at conferences,meet new people in your field, and enjoy the experience. This also counts as research in your residency application and can help strengthen your application. You can find a list of conferences by searching "Medical Conferences" on Google. A site towards the top named MDlinx is typically a good place to look.

QUICK TIPS ON PREPARING A POSTER PRESENTATION:

I was recently a judge for a research day and this experience helped me see a lot as far as what good/bad posters look like. When presenting, you are typically judged on clarity, knowledge base (whether you can answer questions), and poster appearance. When making your poster, don't write entire paragraphs. The LESS YOU WRITE THE BETTER! Put your information in bullet points and put more graphs on your poster. You want to be able to talk about your project without reading it off of the poster. You can find free poster templates by searching "poster presentation template" on Google. The site is called Poster Presentations.

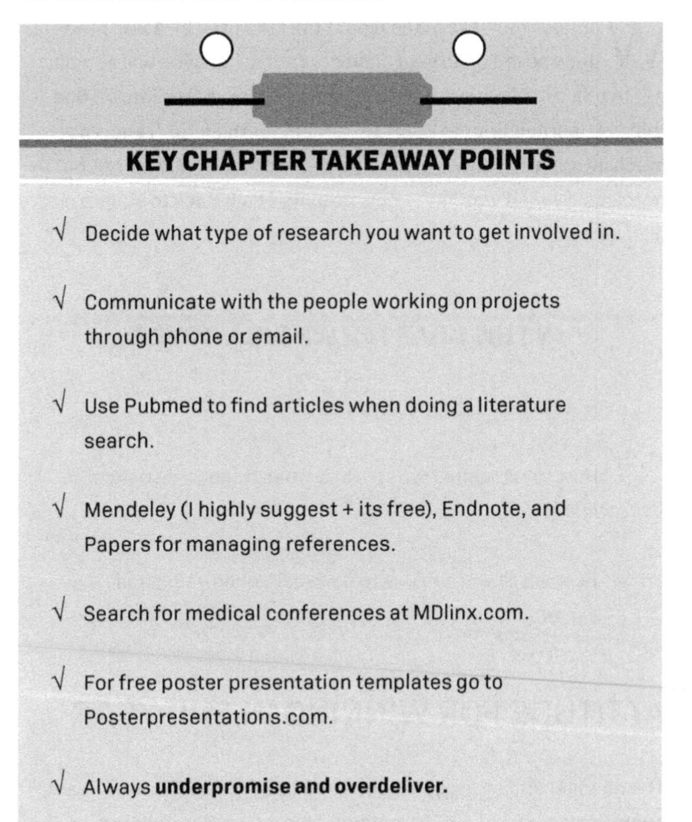

KEY CHAPTER TAKEAWAY POINTS

√ Decide what type of research you want to get involved in.

√ Communicate with the people working on projects through phone or email.

√ Use Pubmed to find articles when doing a literature search.

√ Mendeley (I highly suggest + its free), Endnote, and Papers for managing references.

√ Search for medical conferences at MDlinx.com.

√ For free poster presentation templates go to Posterpresentations.com.

√ Always **underpromise and overdeliver.**

CH 8. THIRD-YEAR/ CLINICALS

Woohoo! You have made it past the land of STEP 1 and have now moved on to your clinical years, where you will actually get to talk to other human beings and use some of the knowledge that you learned prior to STEP 1. I remember thinking "I know so much information now, I'm pretty much a doctor!" and when I got to my clinical year it was like I knew nothing at all! Back to square one all over again.

IN THIS CHAPTER WE WILL COVER:

√ How to beast through 3rd year

√ How to remember what to ask when taking a patient's history

√ Resources you can use to do excellent on your shelf exams

ATTITUDE FOR WINNING IN 3RD YEAR

The mindset and strategy for getting through 3rd year are to learn something new with EVERY patient. This may be learning a new medical condition, a new lesson, or, surprisingly, you may learn something about yourself that you didn't know before.

Listen to EVERY single heart, listen to the lungs every time, and feel for pulses on everybody. The more practice you get, the better you will get, and you will be able to catch when that heartbeat doesn't sound right. You will be able to hear when that lung doesn't sound like it's expanding all of the way and you (the awesome med student) will diagnose a hemothorax and help stop a patient's entire chest cavity from being filled with blood.

An interaction may go like this: "Doctor, my left big toe hurts" "Great!, now let me listen to your heart and lungs and feel your stomach sir!" Learn from the residents and attendings. You are there to learn!

ProTip- Change the words "I have to" to "I get to" and watch your outlook on life change. Listen to the difference between "I have to wake up at 5 AM and drive to the hospital to round on patients today" versus "I get to wake up at 5 AM and go to the hospital and take care of people today." Seriously, how many people get to do that?

HOW TO ASK QUESTIONS WITH A PURPOSE

Getting a proper medical history is a skill that you will need regardless of what specialty you go into. I remember starting off and trying to memorize the entire list of questions and what I had to ask to make sure I did a proper review of systems. I would sometimes end up forgetting to ask certain questions.

I would think to myself, "Did I ask the patient if they had any sneezing? What about shortness of breath when they lay down versus sitting up? I think I may have asked about watery eyes but what about itching? Did I ask about wheezing too or just shortness of breath?" Question overload!!

I remember I was on my internal medicine rotation and I was working with an attending who was notoriously known for being tough to deal with (she who shall not be named). I got what I thought was 100% of the history from a patient and then she would ask me if I asked the patient if she had any sneezing. "No? GO BACK AGAIN!" Ok, I'm back now! "Did you ask them if they have itchy eyes? No? GO BACK AGAIN, SILLY MED STUDENT!"

I must have gone back and forth to the patient's room about ten times that morning. I was getting annoyed by the attending and I wanted to leave the patient alone. The patient was around 70 years old and I'm sure he was getting tired of me bursting into the room to ask yet another question. He was probably thinking "Oh great. Here comes this guy again."

Then, I came to a realization of how to approach each patient and ask the relevant questions and saved myself countless headaches and hours asking questions that didn't really matter.

When you have a patient that comes in for say, chest pain, start to think all of the things in your mind that could cause chest pain. Then think about the signs and symptoms associated with that condition. Then ask your patient the questions that target the signs and symptoms of the conditions on your differential diagnosis list to narrow down your list to what you think it could be.

What you really have to know are the clinical signs and symptoms of different conditions. Build your foundation on this.

Lets work through an example:

DYSPNEA

1. 17 y/o male comes into the ER complaining of Shortness of Breath (Dyspnea).

2. Med student thinks of possible differential diagnosis of what causes shortness of breath. (There are many conditions that cause dyspnea, here are just some):

   - Chronic obstructive pulmonary disorder
   - Bronchial asthma
   - Pneumonia
   - Heart failure
   - Pulmonary embolism
   - Lung cancer
   - Acute bronchitis
   - Airway obstruction
   - Acute coronary syndrome
   - Atrial fibrillation

So now that we have all of these possible causes of what it could be, how do we work through them? In a general sense, some of the condition's onset take a longer time than others (COPD vs Acute Bronchitis).

- Q1 "When did the shortness of breath start?"
- Q2 "What were you doing when the shortness of breath started?"
- Q2 "How long have you had it for?"

With asthma you may expect to hear a history of similar episodes of shortness of breath, you ask:

- Q3 “Has this happened before?”
- Q4 “Do you have any wheezing?”
- Q5 “Do you use an inhaler?”

If a person has pneumonia you may expect them to have some chest pain with inspiration, cough, maybe some sputum production, or a fever so you ask:

- Q6 “Do you have pain when you take a deep breath?”
- Q7 “Do you have a cough?”
- Q8 “Any sputum production?”
- Q9 “What color was the sputum?”
- Q10 “Was it bloody, clear, white?”
- Q11 “How much sputum?”

If a person has heart failure it may be worse when they lay down.

- Q12 “Does anything make your shortness of breath worse? Laying down? What about better?” (All of this time you are ruling in/out possible diagnoses)

You are a detective trying to solve a case. You start out by asking general questions and work through your differential diagnosis list asking targeted questions that help you narrow it down. Having a knowledge base of how different conditions present in your differential diagnosis will help guide you to the kinds of questions you need to ask and can help assist you in remembering what you need to ask.

Another example:

HEADACHE

Patient comes in for headache.

Med student thinks of possible causes of headache:

- Tension headache
- Migraine
- Dehydration
- Tumor
- Cluster headache
- Brain abscess
- Hematoma
- Aneurysm

Now we have an idea of what it could be, let's shift through what it could possibly be.

- Q1 "When did this headache start?" (AKA is it acute or chronic. Cluster headache is less likely if chronic.)
- Q2 "Has this happened before?" (Some headaches are recurrent.)
- Q3 "How bad is the pain on a scale of 1-10?" (A 10 may point towards a more serious cause.)
- Q4 "What type of pain is it? Throbbing, stabbing?"
- Q5 "What part of your head do you feel the pain?" (Certain headaches have certain classical appearances.)
- Q5 "Does it feel like something is squeezing your head?" (Tension headache?)
- Q6 "Does your headache ever wake you up out of your sleep?" (Alarming for tumor.)
- Q7 "Do you have any photophobia?"

- Q8 "Any eye pain?"
- Q9 "A family history of headaches?" (Questions pointing towards migraines). Each question gets us a step closer to figuring out what the problem is.

Old school doctors will tell you that you should be able to diagnose 90% of conditions using just a history and physical exam without other testing. For the most part, they are right. Tests are generally used just to confirm your clinical suspicion.

TIPS ON HOW TO STAND OUT ON ROTATIONS

- Show up early. Leave late.
- Offer to help the residents.
- Work as a team with your other medical students. DON'T BE A GUNNER! Don't throw other people under the bus (People do notice!).
- Be nice to everybody from the janitor, to the attending physician, to the CEO of the hospital. Practice being nice to everybody. Don't disrespect a janitor. Word about that gets around the hospital quickly and can come back to bite you.
- When you get a question wrong, read up on the topic. Pull an article if you want to and come back and talk to the attending the next day. Many students don't do this. It can impress an attending.
- Try to anticipate the resident's needs - if you are on surgery, have supplies for dressing changes when rounding. Have some consent forms ready if they have to be consented.

HOW TO ASK FOR LETTERS OF RECOMMENDATIONS (LOR'S)

DETERMINING WHO

"Chris rotated through my department from the dates of July 1st to August 31st."-Dr. X

That is an actual letter of recommendation (LOR) from an attending physician for a student (Chris) who asked him for one. Chris asked this attending for a LOR even though they barely worked with them or had any type of interaction.

Chris thought that since this person was the chair of the department and is a big name in his field that he would ask for a LOR from this person so it would look good on his application.

WRONG! Don't shoot yourself in the foot like Chris. In general terms, you want to get a letter of recommendation from somebody that knows you well and can attest to your work ethic, enthusiasm, and your knowledge. You want somebody that will fight on your behalf.

They may not always be the chair, but having an outstanding LOR from an attending at your hospital is better than a crappy letter from the chair of the department any day. Ideally, if you can get facetime with a chair of a department that would be great, but ask people who you feel can write you good LOR's. (I really hope that when I said FaceTime you didn't think I was referring to FaceTiming your attending on your iPhone).

HOW TO ASK

Asking for a letter of recommendation **face to face** is better than **calling**, which is better than email, which is better than text messaging.

If you can, always ask somebody in person when asking for letters of recommendation. The upside to asking in person for a LOR, whether or not they can write you a letter, is that you get to see their facial expression and the first response and the little twitches in the face that you would most likely miss over the phone.

You can gauge whether they smile and say "YEAH MAN I WOULD LOVE TO!" versus " You sure? I mean I can write one if you want me to".

If you HAVE to send a request for a letter over email (which I've had to do before too), there are many ways you can do it. Here is a letter that I actually wrote to a physician that wrote me a letter. I requested this LOR after doing a visiting student rotation there. Feel free to use this template:

Good Afternoon Dr. _______________,

I hope all is well. I would first off like to say thank you for having me at _______________ this past month. I learned a lot and was able to gain OR skills as well as deepen my fund of _______________(specialty) knowledge.

During my rotation, I loved working with you and I thank you for all of the teaching and guidance. I actually worked with you the most during my month at _______________ and was wondering if you would be open to writing me a **strong letter of recommendation** for my residency application to _______________(specialty).

If you feel as if you can write me a strong letter of recommendation I would like to thank you in advance for helping me out. If you are unable to for any reason, I also understand.

I have also attached my personal statement and CV to this email if you would like to review it.

Please let me know.

Thank you,

Wendell Cole
Morehouse School of Medicine
Doctor of Medicine Candidate/ Class of 2018
Nth Dimensions Scholar
Cell Number

"Personal Professional Picture"

ProTip: Always state "Do you think you can write me a STRONG letter of recommendation" when requesting LOR's. If they don't think they can, then they just saved themselves time and you from an embarrassing LOR.

HOW TO FOLLOW UP

Give the attending enough time to write the letter. Give them a couple of weeks. I always tell people that I need letters before I actually do because many times they get busy or forget and will submit the letter after your deadline. If you need your letter in 6 weeks, tell the attending you need it in 4 weeks. Also, have a backup writer just in case. You need to remember that people are volunteering their time to write you a letter, so you should you send them reminders. Remember to be respectful.

TOP RESOURCES FOR COMMON CLINICAL ROTATIONS AND BOARD EXAMS

OBSTETRICS AND GYNECOLOGY

√ Case Files Obstetrics and Gynecology

This book goes through different common Ob-Gyn Cases. Pretty self-explanatory.

√ Blueprints Obstetrics and Gynecology

√ Uwise Questions

These are questions directly from The Association of Professors of Obstetrics and Gynecology (APGO). Some medical school Ob-Gyn departments may have a free subscription for students to use to do questions. Check with your department.

√ APGO YouTube Videos

They have dozens of videos on common Ob-Gyn topics, most of them illustrated. Definitely great videos to watch to understand a concept.

√ Uworld Qbank

Yes, the Qbank from STEP 1 is back again, this time covering clinical topics. These questions are always a good resource to use.

√ Online MedEd

An online resource that many third years are now starting to use. They not only cover Ob-Gyn but also cover most third-year rotations. They have videos for free and a paid version with notes that you can use. Many people love it.

SURGERY

√ Surgery: A Case Based Clinical by Devirgillio

One of the best sources I found for surgery. The book is a little harder but has questions that you can do with excellent explanations. I would recommend this book to everyone looking to understand surgery, to do well on the boards, and to ace the rotation.

√ Dr. Pestana's Surgery Notes

A small booklet that goes over many surgery topics. It's an easy read and can be done in a day or so. There are also questions at the end of his book that you can use for practice. He has an audiobook that goes into more detail than the actual book. I used to listen to it while I was walking through the hospital sometimes. Many people use this source!

√ **Uworld Qbank Internal GI**

The shelf exam for surgery historically has a lot of internal medicine questions on it, so doing GI questions on Uworld and being exposed to the material may help you score higher in the exam.

√ **Family Medicine**

This miniboard is a mix of every other subject. Case Files Family Medicine may be a good source.

PSYCHIATRY

√ **First Aid for the Psychiatry Clerkship**

Book, it's great.

√ **Uworld Qbank**

√ **Kaplan Qbank**

PEDIATRICS

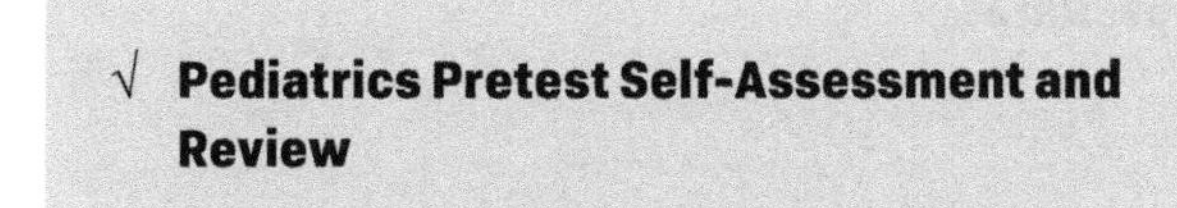

A great question book.

√ BRS Pediatrics

Another great source. It has questions + it covers topics.

√ Online MedEd

INTERNAL MEDICINE

It is important that you understand Internal medicine as it is the majority of your STEP 2 exam and the backbone of medicine!

√ Step Up to Medicine

A good information book.

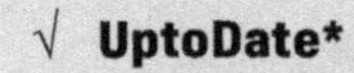

√ UptoDate*

An online, evidence-based resource that many residents and attending physicians use. You can look up different conditions and read up about them.

APPS THAT MAY ALSO BE USEFUL

- **Epocrates (free + upgrade)**
- **Clerkships**
- **AHRQ ePSS,**
- **Prognosis**
- **FP notebook**

KEY CHAPTER TAKEAWAY POINTS

√ Practice your physical exam skills on every patient.

√ Learn something new from every patient.

√ When you hear the Chief Complaint, come up with a possible list of diagnoses to guide your question asking.

√ Be a team player on rotations.

√ Ask for a LOR face to face when you can.

√ A great LOR from a lesser known person is better than an ok LOR from a big name physician.

CH 9.
STEP 2 CS + CK

HOW TO SCORE A 260 ON STEP 2 CK

In many situations, doing well on STEP 2 (CK) can help balance out a lower STEP 1 score. The principles, as far as how you look at questions and go through answers, are basically the same as the STEP 1 exam, so refer to that chapter for guidance (read the last sentence + answers first, and while reading through the question stems formulate your top diagnosis). Here are all of the other steps on how to get a 260 on STEP 2.

1. DO EXTREMELY WELL DURING YOUR CLINICAL ROTATIONS

The key to doing well on STEP 2 is doing well on your rotation shelf exams and being consistent throughout third-year. The majority of the content on STEP 2 comes from Internal Medicine so make sure you have an in-depth knowledge of internal medicine. STEP 2 is no longer about identifying the diagnosis but is about the next best step in the management of patients (actually being a doctor).

2. UNDERSTAND WHAT TESTS ARE REQUIRED FOR DIAGNOSIS AND WHAT THEY YIELD

I started out the year trying to memorize what the test for a specific condition would be without understanding exactly what I was looking for on the test or how the procedure worked. For example, an endoscope. I originally just memorized that you could do an endoscopy to diagnose pyloric stenosis in babies without understanding the rationale of why we would use that test.

At first, I didn't understand that you would first do an abdominal ultrasound (less invasive) and that you could use an endoscopy in cases where it was still unequivocal AFTER an ultrasound was already performed. So, when I saw a question with a baby that most likely had pyloric stenosis and they asked what the next best test was, I messed up and put an endoscopy without question.

When I learned what an endoscopy was and saw that I would be able to visualize the mucosa, see any lesions/growths, and possibly take biopsies, it helped me understand WHY I would use such a test. When I understood what an ultrasound could show and that I could see some of the soft tissue, it helped me figure out why I would use it.

Another example is knowing what a chest x-ray would show you vs a CT scan vs a VQ scan vs bronchoscopy and why you would use any of them. Knowing what the actual test is and how it is performed can help go a long way. What would the harm to this patient be?

You will recognize little things like, well if you are using a bronchoscope, you can take a picture of the bronchioles and take a sample but you probably won't be able to see the small terminal alveoli at the end of the lungs. So if you have a condition that affects the terminal alveoli, what test would you need to use to get a sample?

ProTip: When you encounter a medical test read up on what the test is, how it is performed, what you would look for, and what results the test would yield.

STEP 2 STUDY SCHEDULE

The third year is a different beast than your other two years because you have to juggle studying for class with the schedule of being in the hospital/clinic for the majority of the time. This is where that skill I was talking about earlier comes into play, which is learning how to study with a moderate amount of noise/distraction. Hopefully, you have been slightly developing this skill for the past two years and now you can save yourself some time from studying at home.

Some schools have some dedicated time to take STEP 2 CK and some schools don't. Sometimes you just have to make time yourself. Beyond common belief, it is possible to study in third-year. When I was studying for STEP 2, I woke up and studied before I had to be at the hospital. When I got home, I studied all night (still keeping my minimum of 6 hours of sleep). So a typical schedule looked like this (on a Family Medicine rotation)

6AM-8AM: Wake up + Study

8AM-5PM: Clinic (Study during lunch with my review books, read my quick bullet points which I had in my pocket)

5PM-7PM: Workout, indulge in my daily necessity activities

7PM-11/midnight: Study for STEP 2

= A TOTAL OF 5/6 HRS STUDYING DAILY

(for about a month)

PRACTICE TESTS

I would recommend doing practice tests in the same format as I stated for STEP 1. Do a practice exam at the beginning of your studying a couple months before you plan on taking STEP 2, again in the middle of your study period, and one at the end right before your review time (at minimum). After you take your exam, you will know what areas you are weak in and what areas you are strong in and you can adjust your study schedule accordingly.

1. Calculate the number of days you have from your test date until your exam.
2. Determine which days you want to study (for instance, some people take Sundays off).
3. Determine how much review time toward the end you need (for me it was 10-15%).
4. Once you have an idea of the days you will have to study, create a schedule giving more days to the subjects that you are weakest in (ex: 5 days cardiology, 2 days heme, 6 days pediatrics).

When you make your schedule, I would suggest dividing up Internal Medicine into subspecialties to study so you can be more specific and have targeted study sessions.

ProTip: If you have an iPhone or iPad, take advantage of your free app 'books' and upload your PDF files of books on there. You can literally download the PDF from an email attachment and open it in your books app. Then you will have access to that and can read over it during downtime in the clinic/OR/rotations/ etc. The app Evernote is good as well.

STEP 2 CS

STEP 2 CS is similar to your school's in-house OSCEs. You have a patient that you have to speak to, get a history from, and come up with a list of possible diagnoses and tests to order. Reading the cases in First Aid for STEP 2 CS will take you a long way. Get with a friend and practice going through cases. Remember to do the little things like knock on the door and introduce yourself to the patient. Those are all points.

Pro Tip: Schedule your CS exam early (months in advance). Spots fill up quickly and it may be harder to find an open spot when you want it.

Also, there is a video on YouTube which explains how to approach patients for STEP 2 CS which I found valuable. They call it the 1842 method. I found that by using this method when I took my CS exam, I was generally finished writing my note before everybody else and would be sitting down hanging out until it was time to go to the next room. In general, the method goes like this:

1 minute to read the chief complaint on the door and write down a possible list of differential diagnoses on your piece of paper.

8 minutes to take the patient history.

4 minutes for the physical exam.

2 minutes for the closure.

Following that method saved me time and allowed me to enter the room with a list of questions already in mind to ask to narrow down what I thought my diagnosis was. It also gives you ample time to write down your diagnosis.

ProTip: When writing your note in the computer, start at the end first and write down your top three diagnoses and the tests you will order for each. Then go back and write down the history. Sometimes people run out of time by taking too much time writing down the history.

KAPLAN + UWORLD QUESTIONS QBANKS

What will get you in the best shape for beasting on STEP 2 is doing many questions. The test topics are so broad and diverse that they can ask you a plethora of questions. The more questions you are exposed to the better it is, especially for STEP 2! Along with your books for your overall individual clinical rotations, I would recommend that you get the Uworld AND Kaplan question banks.

WHY?: In my opinion, Kaplan questions are typically a little harder and more specific than UWorld questions. They make you think a little harder and may cover some additional tests and conditions that are not seen in the UWorld question bank. Personally, after doing the UWorld question bank, then doing Kaplan, then going back to Uworld, I felt like the Uworld questions were easier to navigate.

Let it be known, I would score awfully in my Kaplan practice tests, sometimes 30-40% correct, and would get really upset. I would get so frustrated that many times I would stop doing questions. I thought I had a topic down and then here came Kaplan with a left field condition that required me to know 3 different levels to be able to answer the question right! In the long run, getting exposed to the questions put me in better shape to tackle the actual STEP 2 exam.

UWorld - I would definitely buy, and then Kaplan afterward.

ProTip: The same as STEP 1; when you get a question right/wrong, write down in a separate notebook about that topic: how it presents, how you diagnose it, associated conditions, and the different treatment options. Use First Aid for STEP 2 CK as a reference. Take no longer than 5 minutes per question to write this information down.

WHAT I DID DIFFERENTLY FROM STEP 1 TO STEP 2

On STEP 1 I scored a 234 and on STEP 2 I ended up scoring a 259. I'm always asked what did I did so differently, so here are some things that I noted I did a little differently than with STEP 1 that may have explained why my score difference is so high:

1. I had a better overall grasp on conditions.
2. I spent more time understanding the different tests and what they would yield.
3. I read through books with a fine-toothed comb (will touch on which book in the resources section).
4. I found a study partner that was taking the test around the same time as me and we:
    - Would have one person explain an entire topic out loud and the other person would question them on every known possible piece of information on that topic. Asking why this test, why that, what will it show, etc?
    - We reviewed and got together AFTER* we both had done some questions on the topic so we knew what kind of questions would be asked.
    - We both did Kaplan and Uworld questions (She ended up scoring a 264 on STEP 2).

RESOURCES

In addition to your third-year rotation books, here are some good STEP 2 Resources:

1. Master the Boards, STEP 2 CK
    - This is a great STEP 2 REVIEW book. I read the entire book from front to back and took notes on the parts I only DID NOT know, then reviewed my own separate notes every day afterward until the test. I mean, I took notes on every little DETAIL that I did not know. I never re-read a chapter after I went through it.
2. First AID for USMLE STEP 2 CK
    - I would use this book as a reference book for when you get questions wrong.
3. FIRST AID FOR USMLE STEP 2 CS
    - Great book to skim over. Use the cases in the second half of the book.
4. Kaplan Videos
    - Kaplan has some STEP 2 review videos which are great!

KEY CHAPTER TAKEAWAY POINTS

√ Understand the tests and their use.

√ Do as many questions as humanly possible.

√ 1842 Method for successful STEP 2 CS.

√ Read through questions in the same format as stated in STEP 1 chapter.

√ Use First Aid For STEP 2 CK as a reference when doing questions.

√ Keep a separate notebook dedicated only to STEP 2.

CH 10.
18 TIME MANAGEMENT + PRODUCTIVITY TIPS

√ Use Sticky notes.

Get a pack of sticky notes. Write down what you need to get done for the day and put it on your laptop next to the mouse so you don't forget anything.

√ Plan out what tomorrow is going to look like right before you go to sleep.

Whether you do this in your head or use a notes app, before you go to sleep, have an idea of what you did today. Plan out roughly what tomorrow will look like. Write it in a journal if you have to.

√ Play videos & audio on 2x speed.

This saves enormous amounts of time. At first, it'll be a little challenging to understand, but after a while, you will be able to process all of the information. When you go back to listening to videos on normal speed it will feel so slow!

√ Use your notifications app.

If you have an iPhone/smartphone set multiple reminders to keep you on track during your day. You can set an alarm to say 11 AM - You getting stuff done? 2 PM - You still on track? 4 PM - Let's do it, we are in the final stretch. 8PM - Meal for champions. 10 PM - Day well done. That is just an example, but you can customize it however you want. Every day at noon, I have a reminder to myself that "I am the man." If you aren't going to tell yourself that who will?

√ Download the app "Moment" and see how much time you spend on your phone.

It can be a reality check to see how much time you are actually spending on your phone. It's a free app. If you find yourself spending too much time on your phone you can adjust accordingly.

√ Wake up at 5 AM.

The early bird gets the worm. You have a headstart on the day and can accomplish a lot by 8 AM. It gives me a mental win over "the enemy" as Jocko Willink would say, and I feel like I am ahead of the game.

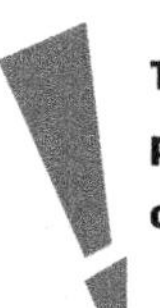

Tips on waking up earlier - go to sleep earlier and put your phone across the room so you have to get up to turn the alarm off.

√ The 1-minute rule:

If it takes less than 1 minute to do, do it right then and there. Put that dish away, send that email, and pick up that piece of trash.

This is hands down one of the best productivity hacks I've come across. It gets rid of all the little clutter in my life.

√ Check your email at set times, once at 11 AM and again at 4 PM.

This way, you aren't checking your email multiple times a day. Get it all done at one time. Set up an email responder for other emails. If it's urgent tell people they can call you on your phone. The one exception during fourth-year when you need to respond immediately to interview invites (refer back to the chapter on Fourth-Year + Residency Resources).

√ iPad Books

If you have an iPad, put the PDFs of your textbooks onto the "books" app. You will have them on the go and can whip it out and read any time you have some downtime.

√ Daily priority list

In your head make a list each day of what you MUST do, what you WANT to do, and what you would LIKE to do if you have enough time. Do the musts first.

√ Study like the test is tomorrow, not 3 weeks away.

You'll get so much more out of your study session.

√ Turn off Notifications.

Turn off your smartphone app social media notifications. They can be distracting.

√ Do Not Disturb

Put your phone on do not disturb when studying or doing an intensive task. You'll get more done.

√ Listen to music.

Focus@Will is a good app that has music that can help get you in the zone. Also if you YouTube "Space Odyssey, deep white noise for focus," there is a 10hr long video of white noise that you can have on in the background that can help you study. Shoutout to Ru for introducing me to this in second-year. I used this plenty of times.

√ Take cold showers in the morning.

There have been many benefits found in taking cold showers in the morning. High achievers like Tony Robbins and Tim Ferriss do this as well or have their own version of it.

√ Learn how to say no.

You can't say yes to everybody. Sometimes you have to say no. Don't feel bad about it.

√ Write in a journal.

Whether it's just a sentence or a paragraph, throw down everything you are dealing with in the journal. It doesn't have to make sense, it doesn't have to be poetry. Just write down what you are thinking. It's therapeutic and helps to clear your mind.

√ Find time to do nothing.

Literally, nothing. Embrace it and just be present. In the midst of being busy and always moving, taking time out to appreciate doing nothing feels great.

CH 11. FOURTH-YEAR/ RESIDENCY

Now that you've made it past the land of STEP 1 and 2, let's talk about our last year of medical school tips.

VISITING STUDENT ELECTIVE ROTATIONS

Generally, depending on what field you go into during your fourth year you have the opportunity to do rotations at other institutions in various fields. Doing an away rotation (visiting student elective) can be beneficial if you are really interested in a particular program and you want to go there. It is basically a month-long interview where you can find out if the program is a fit for you or if you are a fit for the program. In some specialties, it is more common to do away rotations but in others, it isn't really necessary.

For most programs, you schedule away rotations in VSAS - which you typically get access to sometime in the spring. In general here are some tips on VSAS apps:

- Get your immunizations squared away early, delaying on that paperwork may delay you in securing a spot.
- Apply for the rotation as soon as you get access to the dates you want. Some spots can fill up quickly.
- Look on the website of the institution to see if you need any more supplemental forms (sometimes you need to fill out more forms).

CHOOSING WHERE TO ROTATE

A lot of this is specialty dependent, but in general here are some good tips to abide by when you can.

√ **Go where you know at least one person on the faculty.**

This way, you have somebody in your corner and somebody that can (potentially) vouch for you!

√ **Go where you could actually see yourself living.**

Pretty self-explanatory. If you don't see yourself living in Alaska and you are going to a competitive field where it is more common to do away rotations, don't rotate at a residency program in Alaska!

ELECTRONIC RESIDENCY APPLICATION SERVICE (ERAS)

When you apply for residency programs you typically apply through ERAS which normally opens up sometime around September. You can go to Eras.com for the specific dates for when the application will open. In general, here are some tips for ERAS applications:

- Get a seperate Gmail email account for ERAS alone.
- Then download the Gmail app*. Set it up so everytime you get an email you get a notification on your screen and have a

special ringtone for it. The reason behind this is that you want to be notified as soon as you get an email inviting you for an interview. You want to be able to pick the date you want and reserve a spot. Some residency programs will send out more interview invites for interview slots than they have open and students have to reserve them on a first come basis.

- Seriously, this happened to me and my classmate. The program sent out an email and I reserved the interview within a minute, while my classmate was in a surgery and didn't feel his phone go off. By the time he responded to the email an hour later they put him on the waitlist and he never got the interview there. People respond within MINUTES of the email being sent. Download that app!
- Finish Your Personal Statement before you start your away rotations (July/August).
- Have many people review it, including an attending physician IN YOUR FIELD.
- Request for your letters of recommendation by July.
- Give them time to write you a STRONG letter. The earlier you let them know the better.
- Have an updated version of your CV.
- You should be updating your CV throughout all 4 years of medical school. Every time you go to a conference, present at a conference, have a significant community service activity, record it! Don't wait and try to recall everything you did.
- Get a professional headshot for your ERAS application.
- Don't use a cropped Facebook image from Uncle Joe's BBQ last summer where you can see your cousin Billy's hand over your shoulder for your picture. Yes, people really do that.

ProTip: When researching residency programs, Doximity.com is a pretty good source to find more information on a specific program. Also, in many cases, there are specialty specific blogs/forums where people communicate and talk about different programs, interview dates, etc. Ask around for those.

PERSONAL STATEMENT TIPS

A strong personal statement can also make you stand out and help your overall residency application, don't overlook this. I've typically gotten good feedback from my personal statements in the past and it was mentioned to me a couple times on the interview trail. I generally follow the same formula:

- Keep it to 1 page only.
- Start with something to hook the reader (ex: a vivid story).
- Communicate that you have the characteristics to be a good resident without outwardly stating so.
- Communicate why you want to be in that field (sit down and really think deeply about it).
- Communicate what you are looking for in a residency program.

Take your readers through a story. Here is my personal statement below if you need an example. (Be smart and don't copy my statement, come up with your own version).

I almost made it over the hill, but with my next step I slid right back down the pile of sludge and was submerged in the freezing, cold, dirty, muddy water. I rose out feeling heavy and frozen, my eyes were burning. The current mission was to maneuver a 3-ton tree log across a lake of mud with hills and dips and finish by going underneath the sludge as a team. Our muscles ached, we were drained, and the chilly water mixed with the icy breeze made our entire bodies uncomfortable, but we made it through. Many missions and 4.5 hours later I was a proud finisher of my first hurricane heat, Spartan race.

The principles that got me through the race are the same ones that get me through life: determination, teamwork, and one of the most overlooked principles - enjoying the process. Life has taught me that with the right mindset, our bodies are capable of being pushed to the limit and accomplishing great feats but that sometimes we push our bodies past the point of failure and lose the balance between strength and weakness. As an Orthopaedic Surgeon, I want to help people recover their strength and function and regain control over their bodies.

The foundation for my decision to pursue a career in Orthopaedic Surgery was built in childhood. As a child, my family moved around frequently leading me to adapt to new environments on a regular basis. During these difficult times, I often found comfort in fixing things. Taking apart different objects such as DVD players, bicycles, gaming systems and putting them back together gave me a sense of control in an environment where I was constantly being uprooted. Long before I was aware I was developing my coordination, dexterity, and attention to detail, skills critical to Orthopaedic surgery, in the process.

My first introduction to Orthopaedics occurred when I tore my meniscus in high school, and the second when I tore my ACL in college. I watched hours of footage on ACL repairs and became interested in not only how that surgery would help me gain control of my motion and strength, but also how the surgeon would help me to restore my lifestyle. After my ACL repair, I continued to pursue opportunities to learn more about Orthopaedic Surgery. In 2015 I participated in the Nth Dimensions program, founded by the 2015 AAOS diversity award recipient Dr. Bonnie Simpson Mason.

During this time I was able to work with Dr. Clarence Shields at the Kerlan Jobe Orthopaedic Clinic where I participated in a variety of cases and interacted with and learned from the European traveling fellows. I remember the first time I was assisting the Orthopaedic residents in the ER at Grady Hospital during a night shift, to reduce a posterior dislocation of a hip on a 35-year-old man who was in a motor vehicle accident, and realized that this career is what I was meant to do. The gratification and satisfaction of that experience made the hours feel like minutes. I don't see myself doing any other specialty.

Recently, I attended the AAOS conference in San Diego where I learned more about the advancing technology being utilized in Orthopaedics. The procedures from life-altering joint replacements to the arthroscopy used in athletes are exciting, but I will also work diligently to combine my technical skills with a humanistic approach to deliver satisfaction to my patients. I want to be seen as not just as a skilled surgeon but also as a surgeon who cares deeply about the welfare of those I serve. I am eager to train at a program where the residents cooperate effectively, the faculty is made up of enthusiastic teachers, and I can learn the surgical techniques needed to be a proficient surgeon and help serve our community.

As I prepare for the next chapter of my life, I am humbled and extremely grateful to be in the position to be an Orthopaedic Surgery resident. I understand the challenges ahead and that residency will not be a leisurely endeavor, but this is where my last and most important principle comes into play - enjoying the process. Smiling and enjoying the years to come in which I am taking another step towards my internal fulfillment, as well as having a positive impact on society, is what makes everything worth it.

SUPERPRO TIP:

This is such a pro tip that I made it is own mini-section. A couple weeks before you submit your ERAS application, apply for a credit card that gives you SkyMiles. Use that credit card to pay for your application fees (which can be a couple thousand dollars). Different cards have deals where if you spend x amount in the first three months (typically 2-3k) that you may get back 40-50k thousand miles. You will then be able to use those miles to book flights. Pay the card off right away with the money you were going to use to apply with in the first place.

Disclaimer: I am not a financial advisor nor do I claim to be one. Consult your own financial advisor before making any financial decisions.

I was able to use my SkyMiles from cards for at least 5 round-trip flights and an international flight (for vacation) that I didn't have to pay for. Since either way you are going to be spending a bunch of money during your fourth year, why not get some free miles too? Free/deeply discounted flights are always great. I was paying $5 for a round-trip ticket. I got a round-trip ticket to Colombia using only miles (No cash). It's a great travel hack!

Some of the best deals that I have found have been the Southwest airlines card and the Barclaycard. Southwest is great because you can find one-way flights for as little as 5000 miles, and the bonus I had was 50,000 free miles plus 10,000 miles when I refer somebody and they got the card. An honorable mention is the Delta SkyMiles card, but you may just get one or two flights from their card. Seriously - this travel hack saved me tons of money and gave me some additional fourth-year fun.

Pro Tip: If you can, get TSA pre-check. During your interview period, you will most likely be flying around the country a lot. If you have TSA pre-check typically, you get through security quicker (which can save you a lot of time in certain airports), you don't have to take your laptop out of your bag and you get to keep your shoes on. It costs $85, and with all the traveling in fourth-year I found the purchase to be worth it.

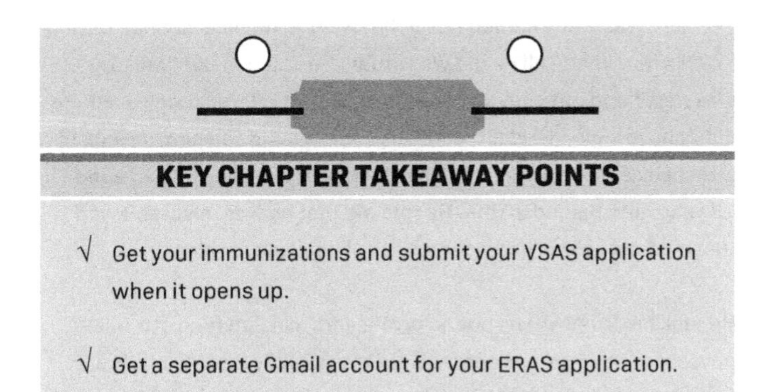

KEY CHAPTER TAKEAWAY POINTS

√ Get your immunizations and submit your VSAS application when it opens up.

√ Get a separate Gmail account for your ERAS application.

√ Get a credit card that gives you a SkyMiles bonus. Use that to pay your ERAS application and enjoy the free miles.

CH 12.
BALANCE

WHAT DOES BALANCE LOOK LIKE TO YOU?

There was a guy named Doug that went to medical school. During his four years, all he did was study. He didn't make time to exercise, hang out with any friends, or go out on weekends at all. He didn't have a girlfriend either. Every time I would see him, he looked stressed. By the end of his fourth year, he looked like he had aged 15 years and gained 30 lbs. He told me that he was miserable and that medical school had been an awful decision for him.

He took his frustrations out on professors, classmates, attending physicians, and his patients too. He was a really cranky guy. His family never really heard from him either. Nobody liked to be around Doug. He ended up just disappearing and nobody heard from him again.

Now... I just made all of that up, but Doug could be you if you don't make time for yourself and your relationships in life. If you're not able to take care of yourself, then it becomes even harder to be able to take care of patients and to do it effectively. It's like that single best friend that you have that has been single forever but gives everybody relationship advice.

Work/life balance is a topic of importance. I mean, many people choose their careers based on work/life balance. It is imperative to say that having a balance keeps you sane. You will be studying a lot in medical school, but you must make time for things that you like to do. At times it can be hard.

Find a hobby that you want to do and do it. Take up the time to sew and do crafts. Take an MMA class or take up some cooking classes. Make sure you have something that you love to do that can make you happy. You start to make your habits of what you're going to be like as a doctor now.

To me, what was important was my health, relationships, school, business, and fun (typically in that order). I knew that without the first two the rest wouldn't be as impactful/possible. So, I made time to make sure I had all of those areas covered and had a balance.

So many times I hear the excuses, "There's just not enough time in the day," or "I'm busy." Stop lying to yourself. Let me break it down for you. You make time for the things that you want to make time for. Simple as that. If you sleep for 6 hours (4 sleep cycles), go to class for 8 hours, and study for 3 to 5 hours, you still have about 5 hours of free time per day! What are you REALLY doing with your time?

Some of that free time can go to cooking/working out/blogging/ etc. My point is, you have more time than you think. You just have to utilize it all.

24hrs/day

6hrs sleep

8hrs class

4hrs study

= 6 HOURS OF FREE TIME LEFT

STRESS

I want to talk about this word stress because these days, we get stressed out about **everything.** I have a very chill and relaxed personality. I barely get stressed out. I remember a woman I was dating would ask me "Are you stressed...how are you not stressed?" and I'd just answer "I have things to do, and I'm behind, but I'm not stressed out about it. I just have to do it." A lot of people ask me "How are you so relaxed? How do you stay so calm when there's a lot of things going on?"

One of the things that I realized is when we look at stress from an evolutionary standpoint, I mean like back in the day when we were all cavemen, we got stressed out when there was a lion right in front of us bearing its razor sharp teeth and it was a life or death situation. Then our sympathetics kicked in, we got that flight or fight response and stress came over us. We also might have been stressed regarding finding food to eat and finding shelter to cohabit.

Having to decide whether or not you are going to get guacamole on your chipotle burrito is not a life or death situation and shouldn't stress us out. I feel like because we don't have those life and death situations anymore, we have other things that trigger our stress response that really shouldn't be stressful.

Stress is worrying about things that are not currently happening. One of the ways to deal with stress is being in the moment. Don't worry about something that is not here. If it's not inherently about to end your life, or you're not in immediate risk or danger, you will be okay. I know this is a newsflash to a lot of people, but you will be okay. Unless you're going to die RIGHT NOW, you can handle it. The test will come, and you will get what you get on it and then life will go on.

For those of you that still do get stressed out, there are a lot of different ways to deal with it.

WORKOUT

Make time to workout, get healthy, and stay physically fit. A study showed that increased stress can lead to decreased functioning of the immune system and make you prone to sickness. It's actually beneficial to workout to decrease the hormone cortisol and decrease your stress levels. There are so many different ways to exercise in a reasonable amount of time. You can join a gym or exercise outside for free.

You can also incorporate it into studying. (I did 5 pull-ups for every UWorld question I got wrong when I was studying for STEP 1). I started out doing 10 pull-ups per question wrong but then quickly realized I was a little overzealous and by question #15 my arms would be gone =[

Here are some free YouTube workout channels that you can do at home in 30 minutes:

Fitness Blender	They are a husband and wife team and have over 800 videos online for different difficulty levels and have a wide variety of workouts.
Popsugar Fitness	She has a lot of dance, yoga, and cardio workouts!
Barstarzz, OfficialThenx, BrendanMyers	These are mostly calisthenics workout channels that I use. I like to workout outside and get some fresh air. They have plenty of routines that you can use at your local park or do at home too.

MEDITATE

Another thing that I realized when I was doing research and looked into the mindset and habits of successful people is that they typically have a morning routine that they do on a daily basis. Many of them use meditation, as do I sometimes. Meditation can get you into a place of relaxation.

It's not like I'm a guru or anything, but you don't have to be a pro at keeping your mind blank to meditate. You don't have to be in a transcendental state for 20 minutes straight with no flowing thoughts. Sometimes thoughts come and go, but if you just have one second of peace during your 15-minute meditation, you did what you were supposed to do. There are a bunch of guided meditations on YouTube that you can use to help you out as well. Here are a couple below:

The Honest Guys	They have meditations and relaxations that you can listen to.
Great Meditation	Another good channel.
Kevin Koh Guided Meditation	Shameless plug, one of my friends that I interviewed did a guided meditation for my podcast. It's about 15 minutes and I use it multiple times a week. My podcast is called Convos With Cole. You can find it by Googling or looking in the Podcast store. It is episode 5.5.

RELATIONSHIPS

Having a significant other is like another part-time job on top of medical school. No joke. You have to set aside time to talk to them, do things with them, and keep them happy. Just so you know, I don't mean a part-time job in a bad sense. You should want to spend time with your significant other and make them happy.

I think the best way to handle a relationship while in medical school is to have them actively involved in your life. Again, if you don't do it now, when will you do it? When you are finally a doctor out of residency?

Here are some tips for having a healthy relationship while in medical school:

√ Have them involved in your school stuff.

This can be with anything. I used to practice my physical exams on my significant other: checking pulses, listening to the heart, knee tests (Lachman exams a bunch too). Have some fun with it, teach them some stuff too. It can be cute.

√ Have them quiz you with notecards.

It depends on how involved your partner wants to get with you, but if they are willing to help quiz you with some notecards, it can be fun. It can help you remember stuff too since you will probably be helping them pronounce the names of some of these diseases and medications.

Have a set date night.

One of my friends always had every Wednesday evening and all day Sunday set aside to spend time with his girlfriend. **No matter what was going on in school** and with everything else, they had time that they knew would be theirs to go out on dates and spend time together. He said it worked wonders.

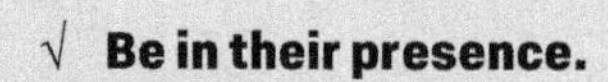

√ **Be in their presence.**

Sometimes just being around the other person can make you feel better, especially if they are helping you out or making you a meal while you study (or stuff like that).

MY STEP 1 BREAKUP

Sometimes it's hard not to let the things that happen in your relationship affect you in your studies. You have to learn how to make that distinction between things that happen in your personal life and school and vice versa.

Here is my little story. I was in a relationship for about four years on and off and about three to four weeks before my STEP 1 exam, something happened and we ended up breaking up and ending the relationship. Nobody knew (except my mom and a friend). I kept it to myself.

Little did anybody know I was so out of it for a while. I was so sad. I was probably clinically depressed around that time. I was scoring low on my end of year miniboard exams in class. Every time I saw a question that mentioned a couple, little tears would come out the side of my eye (sob story, I know).

I'd even be driving my car and a little tear would come out of my eye just from all the pain and the hurt. I was seriously going through it. I was going through all of this while arguably the biggest exam of my medical school career was 3 weeks away; my STEP 1 exam. Talk about awful timing (like the worst timing humanly possible).

One thing I realized is that, as doctors, there will be patients and cases that will affect you personally. The first time you have somebody die under your watch, the time you make a wrong decision and it affects the patient's health, or even watching a newborn child die, can and will mess with your head. You have to learn how to deal with those emotions and not take those same emotions home with you and leave them in the hospital.

So when it came to this I had to realize that I spent all this time and all these years getting ready for this exam that was potentially the biggest exam of my career. This was not the time to mess it up. I had to refocus. I said "Hey, look. I don't know what's gonna happen with this relationship, but I need to focus on this exam. Nothing else at this point is more important." I took all the emotion out of it and had to just think logically for a couple of weeks and I ended up getting it together.

IS A DAILY SCHEDULE REALLY IMPORTANT?

We spoke extensively in this book about schedules, having daily schedules, priority lists, etc. And, it is very important to have that done, but at the same time, life happens unexpectedly sometimes. Tragic things can happen like a family sickness, or your car breaks down, or X, Y, and Z happened and you have to deal with it. One of my classmate's house burned down while we were in medical school!

Sometimes life is going to hit you hard. Like stubbing your toe on the side of the bed in the middle of the night...especially when it's your little toe. How much does that suck?

You are not going to get everything done on time. You have to be okay with this sometimes. Some days, you're just aren't going to feel like studying, and you won't, and you'll be behind. It happens to the best of us. From that point, all you have to do is have the mindset of a champion. **Champions adjust**.

Your schedule is important, but it's not important...and at the same time, it is very important too...

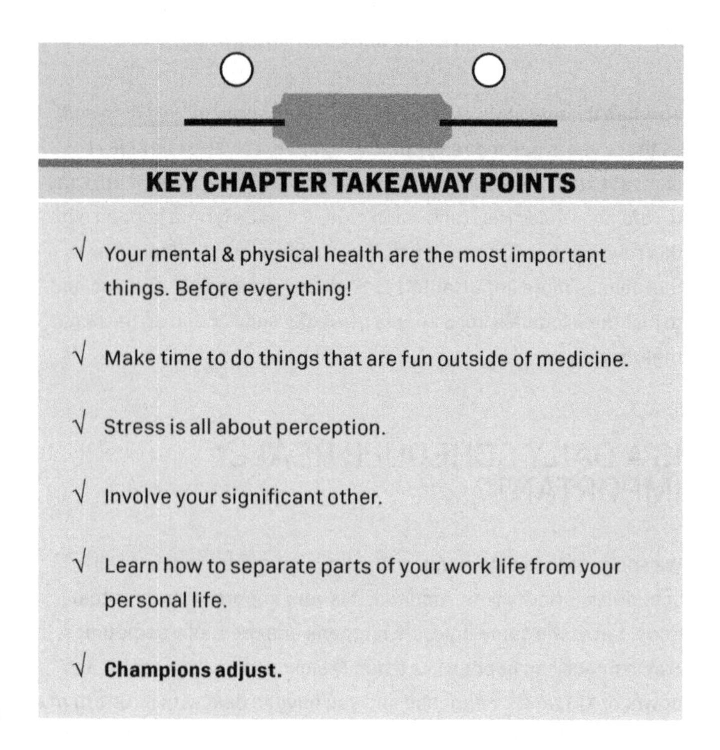

KEY CHAPTER TAKEAWAY POINTS

- √ Your mental & physical health are the most important things. Before everything!
- √ Make time to do things that are fun outside of medicine.
- √ Stress is all about perception.
- √ Involve your significant other.
- √ Learn how to separate parts of your work life from your personal life.
- √ **Champions adjust.**

CH 13. ORGANIZATIONS TO JOIN

There are many different professional organizations you can join while in medical school that can be beneficial to you in the long run. Joining different organizations can help you create networks with different people and provide you with opportunities to present research at different conferences. While there are a lot of organizations, I will name only a couple of organizations here. Also, for a complete list of costs/benefits, you can go to their perspective websites for more information.

1. AMERICAN MEDICAL ASSOCIATION

- You can go to meetings and meet other medical students, residents, and attending physicians. It's great to meet medical students that go to schools other than your own because you get to expand your network and in the future, these will be your future colleagues that you refer patients to. Also, if you plan on doing fourth-year rotations and you know a med student in that city, they may let you stay with them! Money well saved.
- You also get discounts on different things, such as rental cars and Kaplan STEP 2 Qbank (as of 2018). It pretty much paid for itself.

2. YOUR REGIONAL/LOCAL CITY PHYSICIAN ORGANIZATION/THE ORGANIZATION IN THE FIELD YOU ARE INTERESTED IN

- Ex: Atlanta Medical Association, Western Orthopaedic Association, Etc.
- The advantage to this one is you get to meet with people in the field that live in your city, so you will get access to them. You will have the access to talk to them and obtain their knowledge, which could eventually turn into a mentorship and into a letter of recommendation. You may also get chances to work with them one on one which is always a plus.

BONUS: HOW TO NETWORK AT CONFERENCES

As Tim Ferriss would say, "Go deep and long instead of wide and shallow." Typically, when students go to conferences they meet a lot of physicians/residents, maybe get a card, send one email, then they never really continue to foster the relationship. It goes down the drain. You spoke to a lot of people but didn't speak to them about much.

I'd suggest that instead of having the mindset of talking to a lot of people, that you talk to fewer people but get to know them in-depth. Create an actual bond and a relationship with them. Have them invested in you. Go long and deep instead of wide and shallow. Learn about who they are. Do they have kids? How do they like their job? If they could go back in time and change one thing what would it be? This way, when you exchange information, you have something you can refer back to when you reach out to them and you can build that relationship and mentor model.

WHAT IF YOU DON'T KNOW ANYBODY THOUGH?

Getting introduced to somebody by somebody that they trust is a gazillion times better than doing a cold approach. So, this is what you do. If you are at a conference by yourself and don't know anybody, find somebody who isn't the center of attention (the speaker, etc) and go speak to them. "Hey, My name is ____, and this is my first time at this conference and I don't really know anybody here. Do you have a suggestion of anybody you think I should talk to?"

After that, they will most likely ask you who you are and ask some more about you. Then you tell them "I'm a med student at _____ and I'm here to learn and get exposure to the field." After a while, they will introduce you to somebody, and will most likely say "This is ____ from ____ medical school and this is their first time here Dr. Somebody!"

Again, getting introduced to someone that you want to talk to by someone that they already know is the way to go. Then continue to do that and before you know it you will be with a group of people talking. Eventually, they will ask you about yourself and then you can talk about whatever. If you are working on research/interested in research talk about it all!

ProTip: If you do have a business card, put your picture on it. What do most of us do when we get someone's business card? We put it in our pocket. Then days later we have a handful of business cards from different people and don't remember whose is whose. When you have your picture on your business card, it helps you stand out and makes you somebody to remember.

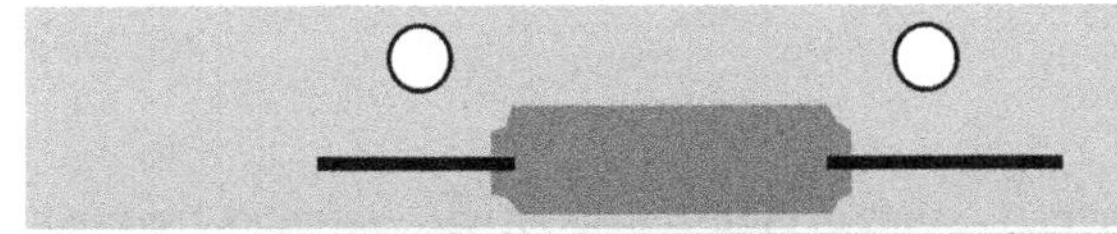

KEY CHAPTER TAKEAWAY POINTS

√ Join the organization that makes the most sense to you.

√ Go to conferences during medical school and make connections.

√ Find your local city medical association and become a member.

√ When "networking," focus on building deeper relationships with fewer people.

√ Get introduced to people by other people when you can.

CH 14. MY MED SCHOOL EXPERIENCE

DAY 1

I remember my first day of third-year like it was yesterday. I started out on a pediatrics rotation on the inpatient service. I was excited for third-year to finally start and I enjoyed working with kids.

That morning, I arrived at the parking lot around 5:45 AM to make it to the hospital by 6 AM. It was still dark outside. I was walking next to Grady Memorial Hospital on my way to the Children's Hospital to do my rotation. I had a fresh haircut, a crisp white coat, a stethoscope around my neck, and my bag with my notebook in my hand.

As I was walking towards the hospital, all of the sudden I heard somebody yell from a distance "Doctor, Help!!" When I heard that I looked around over my two shoulders to see who on earth this lady could be talking to. Then I realized she was talking to me! She thought I was a doctor! I mean, I had on a white coat so it was a fair assumption. I ran over in my uncomfortable dress shoes to this lady as she was jumping up and down calling out to me for help.

Once I arrived she walked me around the corner and I saw a woman having a full-blown seizure in the middle of the street. I mean her entire body was convulsing, her eyes rolled the back of her head, both arms and legs were shaking uncontrollably. I thought to myself "Oh ****"!" I pad my pockets and keep my calm trying to buy a second so I could figure out what to do. I mean, It's my first day. Do I call 911? We are literally right outside of the hospital. She's breathing so I know I don't need to do any CPR.

I tried to think back to when we covered management of seizures, but I had just finished taking STEP 1 so my brain was filled with pathology facts and pathophysiology, not the actual "doctor stuff". As I walk towards this lady having a seizure, an ER doc comes running up at the exact same time and pulls out his toolkit to examine the patient. He checks her pupils, tries to control her, then yells at me to run inside and get the Grady Hospital security guards.

I ran inside and got them. By the time we came back out, there was a sea of people surrounding this lady. Nurses, Doctors, techs, and onlookers. There was also a stretcher and vital sign monitor on its way. By this time she had stopped convulsing, so they brought her to the ER for a seizure workup.

Sometimes It's crazy to realize the power of the white coat and the public responsibility that we are entrusted with. That was literally my first morning of third-year. I don't know why but our role in society to help heal and serve others really sunk in that day. I didn't see myself as a doctor at that point, but to the untrained eye, we are doctors. Many people don't know the difference between the short and long white coats.

I ended up being late on my first day of third-year due to this situation. That in itself was another reminder that medicine is not always planned. You never know when the skill set that you have learned may be needed to save a life. This motivates me, even more, to learn the most I that I can with every patient that I have had and will have for the rest of my life.

My overall medical school experience has been great. It was a breeze for me, in the sense that I still did everything I wanted to do, passed medical school, and landed a residency in the field I desired. I lived life. I went paragliding, jet skiing, volcano hiking, started businesses, all while in medical school (plus much more).

I made friends from all over the country, learned a lot of information, and also gained a valuable set of skills that I can use anywhere in the world to help people. There were some ups and there were some downs, but I wouldn't change my experience for anything. I traveled more during med school than I did at any other time of my life and met more people than I had ever met.

WHAT'S NEXT FOR ME

I am about to embark on the journey of an Orthopaedic Surgery residency. I am finally doing what I've always wanted to do. I know it will be tough and sometimes it will be tiring, but it will also be fun and I will have plenty of new experiences. I mean, I'll get to put nails through people's bones! Who gets to do that on a regular basis?

My advice on picking a specialty is to find the field that drives you and where "work" won't really feel like "work", it will just be fun to you.

Thank you for reading this book and I hope that it helps you breeze through medical school.

INDEX

COMMON ABBREVIATIONS USED IN THIS BOOK

LOR- Letter of Recommendation

PE- Physical Exam

Tx- Treatment

Dx- Diagnosis

OR- Operating Room

VSAS- Visiting Student Learning Opportunities Application Services

PMH- Past medical history

PSHx- Past surgical history

FHx- Family history

SH- Social history

APGO- Association of Professors of Gynecology and Obstetrics

ERAS- Electronic Residency Application Service

GBL- Group-Based Learning

y/o- Year Old

ER- Emergency Room

COPD- Chronic Obstructive Pulmonary Disease

IRB- Institutional Review Board

STEP 2 CS- STEP 2 Clinical Skills

STEP 2 CK- STEP 2 Clinical Knowledge

STAY CONNECTED:

Join the Med School Survivor Community. Connect with each other, share tips and resources and meet each other visit www.medschoolsurvivalkit.com/reader. There may even be special discounts on books/resources exclusively for readers of this book =]

ABOUT THE AUTHOR

Dr. Wendell Cole is an aspiring Orthopaedic Surgeon, author, and a popular podcaster. He hosts two podcasts, Convos With Cole, where he interviews successful people from all walks of life and finds out the stories, mindsets, and routines that make them successful. He is also the co-host of the Orthopaedic Surgery podcast, Nailed It, where they cover topics in Orthopaedic Surgery. With both of his parents being immigrants from the Caribbean, he was able to be the first person in his family to become a doctor and graduate from medical school at the age of 24 years old.

Wendell is also on the E-board of Project Random Acts of Kindness, a nonprofit organization dedicated to helping and empowering the youth and the homeless organizations. He also has a passion for giving back and mentoring those in need.

To learn more about Wendell, go to:

iamdrcole.com/about